9.95

Engineering Materials 2

Engineering Materials 2

W. Bolton

Heinemann : London

William Heinemann Ltd
10 Upper Grosvenor Street, London W1X 9PA

LONDON   MELBOURNE   JOHANNESBURG   AUCKLAND

First published 1987

British Library Cataloguing in Publication Data
Bolton, W. (William), *1933–*
    Engineering materials 2.
    1. Materials
    620.1′1   TA403

ISBN 0 434 90169 5

Typeset by Inforum Ltd, Portsmouth
Printed Great Britain by
Robert Hartnoll Ltd, Bodmin

Contents

Preface

This book provides engineering students and technicians with an introduction to the properties and structures of engineering materials. The aim is to enable the student to appreciate some of the reasons for the choice of material for a specific type of product. The book is planned so as to present a coherent block of study for those requiring only such an introduction, while forming a basis for development for students continuing to higher studies.

The book uses much of the material that appeared in the sequence of books *Materials Technology 2, 3* and *4*, designed to cover the old Technician Education Council units, but this has been completely reorganised and in parts rewritten to more than cover the Business and Technician Education unit Engineering Materials II (U84/265). This unit is an essential feature of all National Certificate and Diploma courses in mechanical and production engineering and other related engineering subjects. Further units develop from this Engineering Materials II unit and are covered in subsequent Heinemann books.

1 The selection of materials

Objectives   At the end of this chapter you should be able to:

- *Recognise the types of factors determining the choice of a material.*
- *State the main properties required of engineering materials.*
- *Compare qualitatively the properties of the different categories of engineering materials.*

THE REQUIREMENTS OF THE MATERIAL

In selecting a material from which a component is to be made, a number of factors have to be considered. These can be grouped under the following headings:

1 The service requirements.
2 The fabrication requirements.
3 The cost.

The main service requirements that are likely to need consideration are whether the conditions under which the component will be used are:

1 Static.
2 Dynamic.
3 Corrosive.

In the static situation the component is subject to forces which vary little with time, whereas in the dynamic situation the forces are fluctuating with time. Thus if the component is, say, a table leg then its conditions of use are likely to be just static, however, if the component is a car drive shaft or leaf spring, then in service there will be both static and dynamic stresses acting on the material.

In a corrosive environment there is an interaction between the material and its surroundings and neighbouring materials which results in degradation of the material. An obvious example of such degradation is rust.

Fabrication requirements can impose constraints on the selection of materials. In the case of metals the main forming methods are:

1 Casting, in which a component is formed by pouring liquid metal into a mould.
2 Manipulative processes, in which a shape is produced by plastic deformation processes.
3 Powder techniques, in which a shape is produced by compacting a powder.
4 Cutting and grinding, in which a shape is produced by metal removal.

The metal alloy that will give a good casting is generally different from the alloy that is used with manipulative processes. A material which is to be shaped by cutting needs good machinability and powder techniques are only appropriate with certain types of materials.

Forming is one way of producing a component. Another way is metal joining, of which the main processes are:

1 Adhesives.
2 Soldering and brazing.
3 Welding.
4 Various fastening systems, e.g. rivets, bolts and nuts.

There is also the wide range of forming and joining methods that can be used with non-metals, the choice of method again determining the type of material that can be used.

In general, the material and fabrication method are chosen on the basis of the lowest total cost (i.e. fabrication and material costs), which is consistent with the required level of performance for the component. There is an interaction between the choice of the material and the choice of fabrication method in determining the total cost. Thus if high dimensional accuracy were required with a large number of items to be manufactured, this would lead to particular processes which would then constrain the materials that could be used. If, for a highly corrosive environment, only a limited range of materials could be used, this would then restrict the choice of fabrication process.

The commercial forms of supply of materials, e.g. as bar, sheet, ingot, pellet, also affects the choice of material and fabrication process. Thus it may be cheaper to form a component such as, for example, a kitchen sink by a manipulative process with sheet than a casting process involving an ingot. The selection of a manipulative process with sheet then limits the choice of possible materials.

PROPERTIES OF MATERIALS

In selecting materials, consideration has to be given to the properties required of the materials for the service environment and ease of fabrication. There are what might be termed general properties, thermal properties, electrical and magnetic properties, and mechanical properties. The following are some of the common ones.

Density
This is the mass of the material per unit volume.

Melting point
This is the temperature at which the material changes from solid to liquid.

Thermal conductivity
This is a measure of the rate at which heat will flow through the material; the higher the conductivity, the greater the rate at which heat will flow through the material. Thermal conductivity is defined by the equation

Rate of flow of heat = thermal conductivity × area × temperature gradient in a direction perpendicular to area

Thermal expansion

The linear expansivity or coefficient of linear expansion is a measure of the amount by which a unit length of the material will expand when the temperature rises by one degree. It is defined by the equation

$$\text{Linear expansivity} = \frac{\text{change in length}}{(\text{original length}) \times (\text{change in temperature})}$$

Specific heat capacity

The specific heat capacity is a measure of the amount of heat needed to raise the temperature of unit mass of the material by one degree. It is defined by the equation

$$\text{Specific heat capacity} = \frac{\text{amount of heat}}{(\text{mass}) \times (\text{change in temperature})}$$

Electrical resistivity and conductivity

The electrical resistivity is a measure of the electrical resistance of the material, being defined by the equation

$$\text{Resistivity} = \frac{(\text{resistance}) \times (\text{cross-sectional area})}{\text{length}}$$

The electrical conductivity is a measure of electrical conductance of the material; the bigger the conductance, the greater the current for a particular potential difference. It is defined by the following equation, being the reciprocal of resistivity:

$$\text{Conductivity} = \frac{\text{length}}{(\text{resistance}) \times (\text{cross-sectional area})}$$

$$\text{Conductance} = \frac{1}{\text{resistance}}$$

Dielectric strength

This is a measure of the highest potential difference an insulating material can withstand without electrical breakdown, being defined by the equation

$$\text{Dielectric strength} = \frac{\text{breakdown voltage}}{\text{insulator thickness}}$$

Relative permeability

This is a measure of the magnetic properties of a material, being defined as the ratio of the magnetic flux density in the material to the flux density in a similar situation when the material is replaced by a vacuum

Strength

This is the ability of the material to resist the application of forces without rupture. The forces can be tensile, compressive or shear. The tensile strength is the most commonly quoted property and is defined by the equation

$$\text{Tensile strength} = \frac{\text{maximum stretching forces}}{\text{original cross-sectional area}}$$

Stiffness
The tensile modulus (sometimes referred to as Young's modulus) is a measure of the stiffness of a material. It is defined as the ratio of the stress to strain in the material when loaded to below the point at which the material begins to yield. It is defined by the equation

$$\text{Tensile modulus} = \frac{\text{stress}}{\text{strain}}$$
$$= \frac{(\text{force/unit cross-sectional area})}{(\text{extension/original length})}$$

Ductility
This is the ability of the material to undergo cold plastic deformation, i.e. show a permanent extension after the stretching forces have been removed. A number of quantities give a measure of ductility, e.g. percentage elongation and impact strength.

$$\text{Percentage elongation} = \frac{(\text{final length}) - (\text{initial length})}{\text{initial length}} \times 100$$

The final length is the length when the pieces are put together after breaking.

Impact strength
This is the amount of energy required to fracture unit volume of the material. It is a measure of the toughness of the material, toughness being defined as the ability to withstand shock loads.

Hardness
This is a measure of the resistance of the material to abrasion or indentation.

Endurance limit
This is a measure of the ability of a material to withstand oscillating stresses. It is defined as the maximum stress amplitude, i.e. the maximum positive and negative stress values between which the stress is alternating, that can be sustained for a stated number of cycles.

Wear resistance
This is the ability of a material surface to resist wear.

Corrosion resistance
This is the ability of a material to resist corrosion.

THE RANGE OF ENGINEERING MATERIALS

Engineering materials can be grouped into four main categories – metals, polymers, ceramics and composites. *Metals* can be defined as being, in the solid form, arrays of atoms held together by 'clouds' of free electrons existing between them (*Figure 1.1a*). *Polymers* can be defined as being materials composed of long-chain molecules, each chain being based on a 'backbone' of carbon atoms (*Figure 1.1b*). *Ceramics* can be defined as being a combination of one or more metals with a non-metallic element; the bonding between the atoms involves the sharing of electrons between atoms, or the

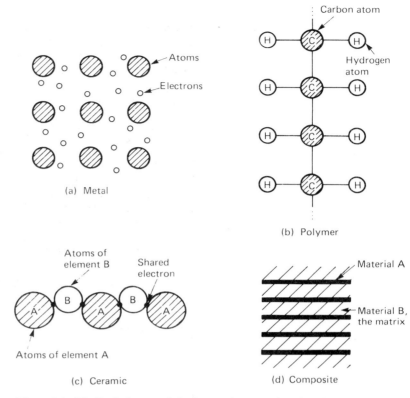

Figure 1.1 Idealised pictures of the four main categories of engineering materials

movement of electrons from one atom to another, and gives a very rigid bond (*Figure 1.1c*). *Composites* are materials composed of two different materials bonded together in such a way that one serves as the matrix and surrounds fibres or particles of the other (*Figure 1.1d*).

The following are examples of the above types of materials.

Metals
Engineering metals are generally alloys, an alloy being a metallic material consisting of an intimate association of two or more elements. There are thus alloys based on iron (steel), aluminium, copper, etc. Metals have high electrical conductivities (hence their use for electrical conduction), high thermal conductivities, and can be ductile, thus permitting components to be fabricated by manipulative processes (this can be crudely put as: they can be bent into shape, as is done for car bodywork).

Polymers
Thermoplastics, thermosets and elastomers are forms of polymers. Thermoplastics soften when heated and become hard again when the heat is removed. The term implies that the material becomes 'plastic' when heat is applied. Thermosets do not soften when heated, but char and decompose. Elastomers are polymers which by their structure allow considerable extensions which are reversible.

Thermoplastic materials are generally flexible and relatively soft. Polythene is an example of a thermoplastic, being widely used in the form of films or sheet for such items as bags, 'squeeze' bottles, and wire and cable insulation. Thermosets are rigid and hard. Phenol formaldehyde, known as Bakelite, is a thermoset, widely used for electrical plugs, door knobs and handles. Rubber is an example of an elastomer. All the polymers have low electrical conductivity and low thermal conductivity, hence their use for electrical and thermal insulation. They have lower densities than metals.

Ceramics

Ceramics tend to be brittle, hard, and chemically inert, and have low electrical conductivity. Ceramics include cements, glasses, refractories and abrasives. Typical applications are cutting tool tips, insulators for high voltage cables, the linings of furnaces.

Composites

Composites include reinforced metals, polymers and ceramics. Reinforced concrete is a composite, being steel rods in a matrix of concrete. Many plastic components are composite materials, involving glass fibres or particles in a polymer matrix. Cermets, widely used for cutting tool tips, are ceramic particles in a metal matrix. Wood is a natural composite consisting of tubes of cellulose bonded by a natural polymer called *lignin*.

THE RANGE OF PROPERTIES

The properties of any one material are generally affected by the treatment it has received and the temperature at which it is being used. Thus, for instance, the properties of metals can be changed by heat treatment, working, ageing and interaction with the environment, e.g. rusting. The properties of a material are also affected by its composition. Adjustment of the relative percentages of the constituent elements, and how they are packed together, in an alloy can markedly affect its properties.

The following table illustrates the range of properties shown by engineering materials.

Property	Metals	Polymers	Ceramics	Composite (wood)
Density/10^3 kg m^{-3}	2–16	1–2	2–17	0.5–1
Melting point/°C	200–3500	70–200	2000–4000	–
Thermal conductivity	High	Low	Medium	Low
Thermal expansion	Medium	High	Low	Low
Specific heat capacity	Low	Medium	High	High
Electrical resistivity	Low	High	High	High
Electrical conductivity	Conductor	Insulator	Insulator	Insulator
Tensile strength/MN m^{-2}	100–2500	30–300	10–400	20–110
Tensile modulus/GN m^{-2}	40–400	0.7–3.5	150–450	4–20
Hardness	Medium	Low	High	Low

The above table can only roughly indicate the types of properties that might be expected from a material. More specific information on some materials is given in Chapter 2.

PROBLEMS   1 Explain what is meant by the term 'service requirements' when used in considering the choice of a material for a component.

2 What types of service requirements would occur with the following components?

(a) A domestic kitchen sink.

(b) An aircraft undercarriage.

(c) A shelf in a bookcase.

(d) A conveyor belt.

3 What characteristics of a material are decribed by the following properties?

(a) Density.

(b) Thermal conductivity.

(c) Electrical conductivity.

(d) Tensile modulus.

4 Which properties of materials would you need to consider if you required materials which were:

(a) stiff

(b) a heat insulator

(c) capable of being bent into a fixed shape

(d) capable of being used as the lining for a tank storing acid.

5 Explain what types of materials are (a) metals, (b) polymers, (c) ceramics, and (d) composites, giving a rough definition of each category.

6 How do thermoplastics differ from thermosets?

7 Describe in a qualitative manner the main properties of metals, polymers, ceramics and a composite such as wood.

8 Give typical engineering applications of metals, thermoplastics, thermosets, elastomers, ceramics and wood.

2 Properties of materials

Objectives At the end of this chapter you should be able to:

● *Describe the main methods used for tensile testing, impact testing, bend tests and hardness measurements, interpreting the results of such measurements.*
● *Interpret thermal conductivity and electrical conductivity data.*

THE TENSILE TEST FOR METALS

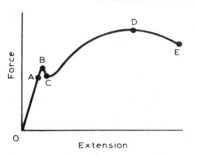

Figure 2.1 The form of a typical force-extension graph for a metal, e.g. a low carbon steel

In a tensile test, measurements are made of the force required to extend a standard size test piece at a constant rate, the elongation of a specified gauge length of the test piece being measured by some form of extensometer. The measurements thus obtained from the test are those of force applied and resulting extension. *Figure 2.1* shows the form of a typical force-extension graph for a metal.

For the part of the force-extension graph 0A the extension is directly proportional to the force. *Hooke's law* is said to be obeyed. Point A is called the *limit of proportionality*. Up to a certain force the material will return to its original dimensions when the force is removed, the region of the force-extension graph for which this occurs is called the *elastic region*. The maximum force for which this occurs is called the elastic limit. For many materials the elastic limit and limit of proportionality are almost identical.

Beyond the elastic limit the material will not return to its original dimensions when the force is removed, the material retaining a permanent change in dimensions. This is referred to as a *permanent set* or *plastic deformation*.

Beyond the limit of proportionality the extension is no longer proportional to the force. In some materials a situation may arise where the extension continues to increase without any increase in force; this point is known as the *yield point*. For the graph shown in *Figure 2.1*, typical of a low carbon steel, there are two distinct yield points B and C. Point B is called the *upper yield point*, point C the *lower yield point*. In data given of just yield points, with no distinction between upper and lower points, the values given are for the lower yield points.

After the yield points have been passed, an increase in force is necessary for an increase in extension; however the two are not proportional to each other. At point D the force is a maximum, after that the force decreases though the extension increases until point E is reached when the material breaks.

In order that the data obtained from one particular cross-sectional area test piece can be applied to other cross-sectional area pieces of the same material, the force information is presented as the *stress*. This stress is the force divided by the initial cross-sectional area of the test piece. The extensions are also presented as *strain*, the extension divided by the initial gauge length. The force-extension graph can thus be used to obtain the more general stress–strain graph. For stress and strain defined as above the stress-strain graph will be of the same form as the force-extension graph

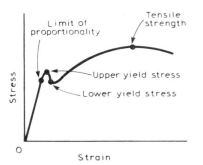

Figure 2.2 Stress–strain graph for *Figure 2.1*

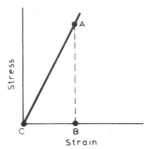

Figure 2.3 Young's modulus, or tensile modulus as it is often called, equals AB/BC

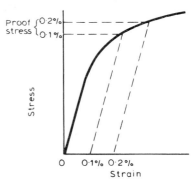

Figure 2.4 Determination of proof stress

with just the force values divided by the initial cross-sectional area and the extension values divided by the initial gauge length (*Figure 2.2*).

For a tensile stress–strain graph the term *tensile strength* is used for the maximum force (point D on *Figure 2.1*) divided by the initial cross-sectional area of the test piece. The slope of the stress–strain graph up to the limit of proportionality, i.e. stress/strain, is called the *tensile modulus* or *Young's modulus* (*Figure 2.3*).

Many materials do not have well-defined yield points, their stress–strain graph being of the form shown in *Figure 2.4*. In such instances a *proof stress* is specified rather than a yield stress. The 0.2% proof stress is defined as that stress which results in a 0.2% offset, i.e. the stress given by a line drawn on the stress–strain graph parallel to the linear part of the graph and passing through the 0.2% strain value. Similarly the 0.1% proof stress is given by drawing a line on the stress–strain graph parallel to the linear part of the graph and passing through the 0.1% strain value.

Other data is also often obtained during a tensile test. After the test piece has broken, the pieces are fitted together and the final gauge length measured. With the initial gauge length, this enables a quantity called the *percentage elongation* to be calculated.

$$\text{Percentage elongation} = \frac{\text{(final length)} - \text{(initial length)}}{\text{initial length}} \times 100$$

Similarly, another quantity called the *percentage reduction in area* can be determined from the initial cross-sectional area and the smallest cross-sectional area at fracture.

The tensile properties of metals depend on the temperature at which the data was obtained. In general the tensile modulus and the tensile strength both decrease with an increase in temperature. The percentage elongation tends to increase with an increase in temperature (see the example with *Figure 2.19*).

The data obtained from a tensile test are affected by the rate at which the test piece is strained, so in order to give standardised results, tensile tests are usually carried out at a constant strain rate. For metals tested at room temperature, the standard rate specified in BS 18 is a strain of 0.5 per minute or less.

Example

Figure 2.5 shows the stress–strain graph for a sample of mild steel. Determine (a) the limit of proportionality, (b) the upper yield point, (c) the lower yield point and (d) the tensile strength.

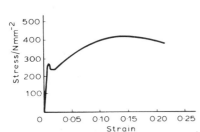

Figure 2.5 Stress–strain graph for a sample of mild steel

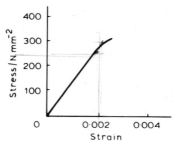

Figure 2.6 Stress–strain graph for a sample of cast iron

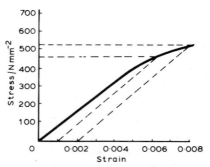

Figure 2.7 Part of the stress–strain graph for a sample of an aluminium alloy

(a) The limit of proportionality is about 240 N mm⁻².
(b) The upper yield point is about 280 N mm⁻².
(c) The lower yield point is about 240 N mm⁻².
(d) The tensile strength is about 400 N mm⁻².

Example
Figure 2.6 shows the stress–strain graph for a sample of cast iron. Determine Young's modulus for the sample.
Young's modulus is about 125 kN mm⁻².

Example
Figure 2.7 shows the stress–strain graph for a sample of an aluminium alloy. Determine (a) the 0.1% proof stress, (b) the 0.2% proof stress.
(a) The 0.1% proof stress is about 460 N mm⁻².
(b) The 0.2% proof stress is about 520 N mm⁻².

Example
A sample of mild steel had an initial gauge length of 69 mm. After breaking, the gauge length had become 92 mm. What is the percentage elongation?

$$\text{Percentage elongation} = \frac{(\text{final length}) - (\text{initial length})}{\text{initial length}} \times 100$$

$$= \frac{92-69}{69}$$

$$= 33\%$$

THE TENSILE TEST PIECE

In order to eliminate any variations in tensile test data due to differences in the shapes of test pieces, standard shapes are adopted. *Figure 2.8* shows the forms of two standard test pieces, one being a flat test piece and the other a round test piece. The following are the dimensions of some standard test pieces:

Flat test pieces

b/mm	L_o/mm	L_c/mm	L_t/mm	r/mm
25	100	125	300	25
12.5	50	63	200	25
6	24	30	100	12
3	12	15	50	6

Round test pieces

A/mm²	d/mm	L_o/mm	L_c/mm	r/mm Wrought material	r/mm Cast material
200	15.96	80	88	15	30
150	13.82	69	76	13	26
100	11.28	56	62	10	20
50	7.98	40	44	8	16
25	5.64	28	31	5	10
12.5	3.99	20	21	4	8

(The information in the above tables was extracted from BS 18.)

For the tensile test data for the same material to give essentially the same stress–strain graph, regardless of the length of the test piece used, it is vital that the above standard dimensions be adhered to. An important feature of the dimensions is the radius given for

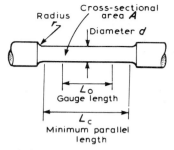

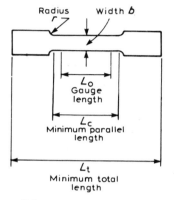

(a) Round test piece

(b) Flat test piece

Figure 2.8 Tensile test pieces, (a) round test piece, (b) flat test piece

the shoulders of the test pieces. Variations in the radii can affect markedly the tensile test data. Very small radii can cause localised stress concentrations which may result in the test piece failing prematurely. The surface finish of the test piece is also important for the same reason.

The round test pieces are said to be *proportional test pieces*, for which the relationship between the gauge length L_o and the cross-sectional area of the piece A is specified in the relevant British Standard as being

$$L_o = 5.65 \sqrt{A}$$

With circular cross-sections $A = \frac{1}{4}d\pi^2$ the relationship becomes, to a reasonable approximation

$$L_o = 5d$$

The reason for the specification of a relationship between the gauge length and the cross-sectional area of the test piece is in order to give reproducible test results for the same test material when different size test specimens are used. When a ductile material is being extended in the plastic region of the stress–strain relationship, the cross-sectional area of the piece does not reduce uniformly but necking occurs (*Figure 2.9*). The effect of this is to cause most of the further plastic deformation to occur in the necked region where the cross-sectional area is least. The percentage elongation can thus differ markedly for different gauge lengths encompassing this necked portion of the test piece (*Figure 2.10*). Doubling the gauge length does not double the elongation because most of the elongation is in such a small part of the gauge length. The same percentage elongation is however given if

$$\frac{\text{gauge length}}{\sqrt{(\text{cross-sectional area})}} = \text{a constant}$$

In England the constant is chosen to have the fixed value of 5.65.

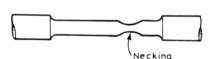

Figure 2.9 Necking of a tensile test piece

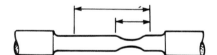

Figure 2.10 The percentage elongation for the two different gauge lengths differ considerably

The tensile test piece is usually chosen so that its properties are indicative of the properties of a component or components. This can present problems if the properties of a component are not the same in all parts of it. There can be a problem with a casting where the properties of the casting material may not be the same as that of a specially cast test piece, because of the different sizes of the two and hence the different cooling rates. Care has thus to be taken in interpreting the results of tensile test pieces.

THE TENSILE TEST FOR PLASTICS

Tensile tests can be used with plastic test pieces to obtain stress–strain data. The term tensile strength has the same meaning as with metals. The tensile modulus, i.e. Young's modulus can be determined in the same way as with metals, i.e. the slope of the

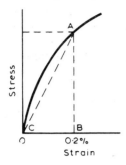

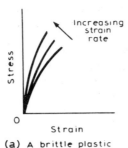

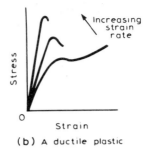

(a) A brittle plastic

(b) A ductile plastic

Figure 2.11 Part of the stress–strain graph for a plastic. The secant modulus is AB/BC, i.e. the slope of the line AC

Figure 2.12 The effect of strain rate on the stress–strain graphs for plastics, (a) a brittle plastic, (b) a ductile plastic

stress–strain graph for stresses below the limit of proportionality. For many plastics there is, however, no straight-line part of the stress–strain graph and thus the tensile modulus cannot be determined in the way specified for metals. In such cases it is common practice to quote a modulus, termed the *secant modulus*, which is obtained by dividing the stress at a value of 0.2% strain by that strain (*Figure 2.11*).

The stress–strain properties of plastics are much more dependent on the rate at which the strain is applied than metals. Thus, for example, the stress–strain data may indicate a yield stress of 62 N mm^{-2} when the rate of elongation is 12.5 mm/min but 74 N mm^{-2} when it is 50 mm/min. *Figure 2.12* shows the general forms of stress–strain graphs for plastics at different strain rates. Another factor that has a considerable effect on the stress–strain properties of plastics is temperature. *Figure 2.13* shows how the tensile modulus tends to vary with temperature for plastics.

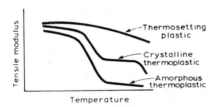

Figure 2.13 The effect of temperature on the tensile modulus of plastics

Example
Figure 2.14 is the stress–strain graph for a sample of ABS Novodur grade PK (courtesy of Bayer (UK) Ltd). Estimate (a) the tensile modulus and (b) the tensile strength.

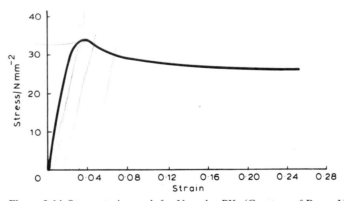

Figure 2.14 Stress–strain graph for Novodur PK. (Courtesy of Bayer UK Ltd)

(a) The tensile modulus is about 1.4 kN mm^{-2} when estimated from the graph.

(b) The tensile strength is about 34 N mm^{-2} estimated from the graph.

INTERPRETING TENSILE TEST DATA

Figure 2.15 shows the types of stress–strain graph produced by brittle and ductile materials. *Brittle* materials show little plastic deformation before fracture, *ductile* materials show a considerable amount of plastic deformation. If you drop a china tea cup and it breaks you can stick the pieces together again and still have the same tea cup shape. The material used for the tea cup is a brittle material and little, if any, plastic deformation took place prior to fracture. If the wing of a motor car is involved in a collision it is likely to show considerable deformation rather than a fracture. The mild steel used in the car body work is a ductile material.

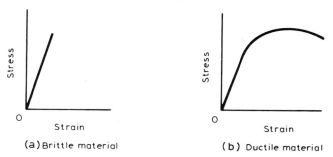

Figure 2.15 Stress–strain graphs to fracture, (a) brittle material, (b) ductile material.

A brittle material will show only a small percentage elongation, i.e. the length of the specimen is very little different from the initial length as little plastic deformation has occurred (*Figure 2.16*). The material also shows little, if any, sign of necking. A ductile material, however, shows quite a large percentage elongation and quite significant necking.

Grey cast iron is a brittle material, it has a percentage elongation of about 0.5 to 0.7%. Mild steel is a reasonably ductile material and has a percentage elongation of the order of 30%.

Thermosetting plastics tend to behave as brittle materials. Thermoplastic materials can be either brittle or ductile depending on the temperature. Melamines are thermosetting materials and have percentage elongations of about 1% or less. High density polythene, a thermoplastic, can have percentage elongations as high as 800%.

The tensile modulus of a material can be taken as a measure of the stiffness of the material. The higher the value of the modulus the stiffer the material, i.e. the greater the force needed to produce a given strain within the limit of proportionality region (*Figure 2.17*). Mild steel has a tensile modulus of about 200 kN mm^{-2} while an aluminium alloy may have a modulus of 70 kN mm^{-2}. A strip of mild steel is thus stiffer than a corresponding strip of aluminium alloy. Plastics have relatively low tensile modulus values when compared with metals, e.g. polythene has a modulus of about 0.1 to 1.2 kN mm^{-2}.

The strength of a material is indicated by its tensile strength. An alloy steel may have a strength as high as 1500 N mm^{-2}, while an aluminium alloy may only have a strength of 200 N mm^{-2}. The steel is obviously much stronger than the aluminium alloy. Plastics have tensile strengths lower than those of metals, though their strengths can be increased by incorporating fillers in the plastic. Polythene has a tensile strength of between 4 and 38 N mm^{-2}.

Figure 2.16

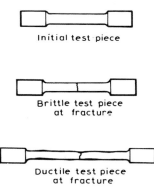

Figure 2.17 Stress–strain graphs within the limit of proportionality region

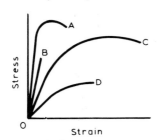

Figure 2.18

Example

Which of the materials shown in *Figure 2.18* is (a) the most ductile, (b) the most brittle, (c) the strongest, (d) the stiffest?

(a) Material C, (b) Material B, (c) Material A, (d) Material A.

Example

Which of the following materials is the most ductile?

Material	Percentage elongation %
80–20 brass	50
70–30 brass	70
60–40 brass	40

The most ductile material is the one with the largest percentage elongation, i.e. the 70–30 brass.

Example

Which of the following plastics is (a) the stiffest, (b) the strongest in tension?

Material	Tensile modulus /kN mm^{-2}	Tensile strength /N mm^{-2}
ABS	2.5	38
Polycarbonate	2.8	60
Polypropylene	1.3	30
PVC	3.1	50

(a) The stiffest plastic is the one with the highest tensile modulus, i.e. the PVC.

(b) The strongest plastic is the one with the highest tensile strength, i.e. the polycarbonate.

Example

Figure 2.19 shows how the tensile strength and percentage elongation varies with temperature for a carbon steel. At what temperature is the steel (a) strongest, (b) least ductile?

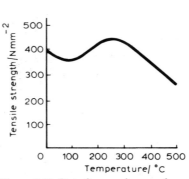
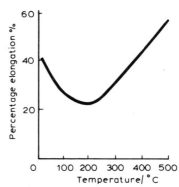

Figure 2.19 Data for a carbon steel

(a) The steel is strongest at a temperature of about 250°C, within the range for which the data is given.

(b) The steel is least ductile at a temperature of about 200°C, within the range for which the data is given.

TYPICAL TENSILE TEST RESULTS   The following table gives typical tensile strength and tensile modulus values for metals and plastics.

Material	Tensile strength /N mm^{-2}	Tensile modulus /kN mm^{-2}
Aluminium alloys	100 to 550	70
Copper alloys	200 to 1300	110
Magnesium alloys	150 to 350	45
Nickel alloys	400 to 1600	200
Titanium alloys	400 to 1600	100
Zinc alloys	200 to 350	100
Grey cast iron	150 to 400	100
Mild steel	350 to 500	200
Ferritic stainless steel	500 to 600	200
Martensitic stainless steel	450 to 1300	200
Polythene, low-density	8–16	0.2
Polythene, high-density	22–38	0.9
PVC, no plasticiser	52–58	2.7
Polystyrene	35–60	3.3
Nylon 6	70–90	2.2
Wood	50–100	10–20

IMPACT TESTS

Impact tests are designed to simulate the response of a material to a high rate of loading, and involve a test piece being struck a sudden blow. There are two main forms of test, the *Izod* and *Charpy* tests. Both tests involve the same type of measurement but differ in the form of the test pieces. Both involve a pendulum swinging down from a specified height to hit the test piece (*Figure 2.20*). The height to which the pendulum rises after striking and breaking the test piece is a measure of the energy used in the breaking. If no energy were used the pendulum would swing up to the same height as it started from. The greater the energy used in the breaking the lower the height to which the pendulum rises.

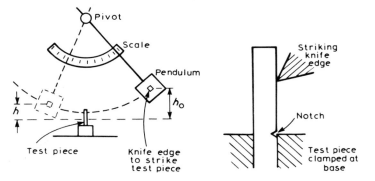

Figure 2.20 The principle of impact testing

Figure 2.21 Form of the Izod test piece (elevation view)

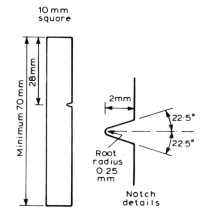

Figure 2.22 British Standard Izod test piece for a metal

With the Izod test the energy absorbed in breaking a cantilevered test piece (*Figure 2.21*) is measured. The test piece has a notch and the blow is struck on the same face of the piece as the notch is and at a fixed height above it. The test pieces used are, in the case of metals, either 10 mm square or 11.4 mm diameter if they conform to British Standards (BS 131: Part 1). *Figure 2.22* shows the details of a test piece conforming to British Standards. The British Standard test pieces for plastics (BS 2782: Part 3) are either 12.7 mm square or 12.7 mm by 6.4 to 12.7 mm depending on the thickness of the material concerned (*Figure 2.23*). With metals the pendulum strikes the test piece with a speed between 3 and 4 m/s, with plastics this speed is 2.44 m/s.

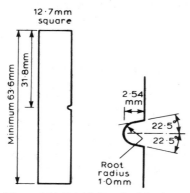

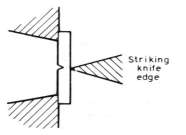

Figure 2.23 British Standard Izod test piece for a plastic

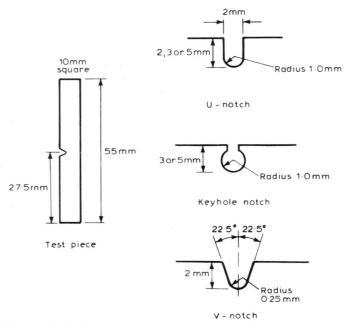

Figure 2.24 Form of the Charpy test piece (plan view)

With the Charpy test the energy absorbed in breaking a beam test piece (*Figure 2.24*) is measured. The test piece is supported at each end and is notched in the middle between the two supports. The notch is on the face directly opposite to where the pendulum strikes the test piece. For metals the British Standard test piece has a square cross-section of side 10 mm and a length of 55 mm (BS 131: Parts 2 and 3). *Figure 2.25* shows the details of a standard test piece and the three forms of notch that are possible. The results obtained with the different forms of notch cannot be compared; for comparison purposes between metals, the same type of notch should be used. The test pieces for plastics are tested either in the notched or un-notched state. The notch is produced by milling a slot across one face, the slot of width 2 mm having a radius of less than 0.2 mm at the corners of the base and the walls of the slot. A standard test piece is 120 mm long, 15 mm wide and 10 mm thick in the case of moulded plastics. Different widths and thicknesses are used with sheet plastics. With metals the pendulum strikes the test piece with a speed between 3 and 5.5 m/s, with plastics the speed is between 2.9 and 3.8 m/s.

The results of impact tests need to specify not only the type of test, i.e. Izod or Charpy, but the form of the notch used. In the case of metals the results are expressed as the amount of energy absorbed by the test piece when it breaks. The results for plastics however are often given as absorbed energy divided by either the cross-sectional area of the un-notched test piece or the cross-sectional area behind the notch in the case of notched test pieces.

Another test that is sometimes used with plastics involves a weight falling on to a disc of the material under test. The disc for the British Standard test (BS 2782), is 57 to 64 mm in diameter, or a square of 57 to 64 mm side resting on an annular support of 50.8 mm inner diameter and maximum external diameter of 57.2 mm. The

Figure 2.25 British Standard Charpy test piece for a metal

thickness of the test piece is 1.52 mm in the case of moulded plastics. The impact strength is the energy needed to fracture half of a large number of samples of the material.

Example

In an Izod test the pendulum in falling acquires a kinetic energy of 160 J before striking the test piece. If after fracturing the test piece the pendulum continues up to a height of 60% of that from which it started its motion, what is the energy used to fracture the piece?

The kinetic energy of the pendulum, after striking the test piece and breaking it, is transformed into potential energy. This potential energy is 60% of the potential energy with which the pendulum started. Thus 40% of the energy was used to break the test piece, i.e. 64 J.

INTERPRETING IMPACT TEST RESULTS

The fracture of materials can be classified roughly as either brittle or, ductile fracture. With *brittle fracture* there is little, or no, plastic deformation prior to fracture. With *ductile fracture* the fracture is preceded by a considerable amount of plastic deformation. Less energy is absorbed with a brittle fracture than with a ductile fracture. Thus Izod and Charpy test results can give an indication of the brittleness of materials.

The appearance of the fractured surfaces after an impact test also gives information about the type of fracture that has occurred. With a brittle fracture of metals the surfaces are crystalline in appearance, with ductile fracture the surfaces are rough and fibrous in appearance. Also with a ductile failure there is a reduction in the cross-sectional area of the test piece, but with a brittle fracture there is virtually no change in the area. With plastics a brittle failure gives fracture surfaces which are smooth and glassy or somewhat splintered, with a ductile failure the surfaces often have a whitened appearance. With plastics the change in cross-sectional area can be considerable with a ductile failure.

One use of impact tests is to determine whether heat treatment has been successfully carried out. A comparatively small change in heat treatment can lead to quite noticeable changes in impact test results. The changes can be considerably more pronounced than changes in other mechanical properties, e.g. percentage elongation or tensile strength. *Figure 2.26* shows the effect on the Izod impact test results for cold worked mild steel annealed to different temperatures. The use of an impact test could then indicate whether annealing has been carried out to the correct temperature.

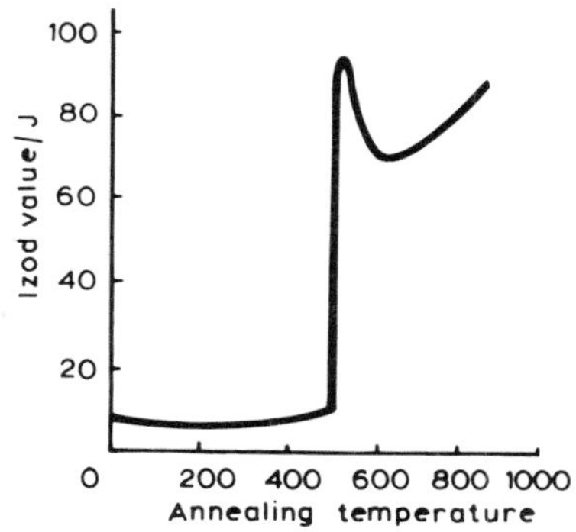

The properties of metals change with temperature. For example, a 0.2% carbon steel undergoes a gradual transition from a ductile to a brittle material at a temperature of about room temperature (*Figure 2.27*). At about −25°C the material is a brittle material with a Charpy V-notch impact energy of only about 4 J, whereas at about 100°C it is ductile with an impact energy of about 120 J. This type of change from a ductile to a brittle material can be charted by impact test results and the behaviour of the material at the various temperatures predicted.

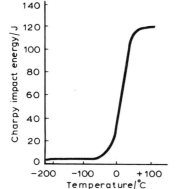

Figure 2.26 Effect of annealing temperature on Izod test values

Figure 2.27 Effect of temperature on the Charpy V-notch impact energies for a 0.2 per cent carbon steel

Example

A sample of unplasticised PVC has an impact strength of 3 kJ m^{-2} at 20°C and 10 kJ m^{-2} at 40°C. At what temperature is the material most brittle?

The more brittle a material the lower the amount of energy absorbed. The material is thus more brittle at 20°C than 40°C.

Example
A structural steel gives a Charpy V-notch impact energy value of 27 J at room temperature. When the temperature drops to below 0°C this value decreases and at temperatures of −20°C it is considerably lower. Is the steel becoming more brittle or more ductile as the temperature falls?
The steel is becoming more brittle.

TYPICAL IMPACT TEST RESULTS   The following table gives typical impact test results for metals and plastics at 0°C.

Material	Charpy V impact strength/J
Aluminium, commercial pure, annealed	30
Aluminium–1.5% Mn alloy, annealed	80
hard	34
Copper, oxygen free HC, annealed	70
Cartridge brass (70% Cu, 30% Zn), annealed	88
¾ hard	21
Cupronickel (70% Cu, 30% Ni), annealed	157
Magnesium–3% Al, 1% Zn alloy, annealed	8
Nickel alloy, Monel, annealed	290
Titanium–5% Al, 2.5% Sn, annealed	24
Grey cast iron	3
Malleable cast iron, Blackheart, annealed	15
Austenitic stainless steel, annealed	217
Carbon steel, 0.2% carbon, as rolled	50

Material	Impact strength*/kJ m^{-2}
Polythene, high-density	30
Nylon 6.6	5
PVC, unplasticised	3
Polystyrene	2
ABS	25

*Notch-tip radius 0.25 mm, depth 2.75 mm

BEND TESTS   The *bend test* is a simple test of ductility. It involves bending a sample of the material through some angle and determining whether the material is unbroken and free from cracks after such a bend. *Figure 2.28* shows one way of conducting a bend test. The results of a bend test are specified in terms of the angle of bend (*Figure 2.29*).

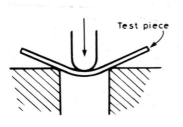

Figure 2.28 A bent test

Figure 2.29 The angle of bend

The following data is taken from a manufacturer's brochure (courtesy of Arthur Lee & Sons Ltd) and illustrates the type of information given for bend tests.

Tempers – mild steel
CS4 Hard
For maximum strength where no bending or drawing is involved.
For clean and crisp shearing or blanking.

CS4 Half Hard
Strip will stand a 90° transverse bend over a radius equal to its
own thickness. Useful for simple bending operations.
CS4 Quarter Hard
Strip will stand a close bend in the transverse direction and 90°
longitudinal bend over a radius equal to its own thickness.
CS4 Annealed (Dead Soft)
Strip will stand being bent flat on itself in both directions, and can
also be used for simple pressing and drawing.

HARDNESS MEASUREMENTS WITH METALS

The *hardness* of a material may be specified in terms of some
standard test involving indentation or scratching of the surface of
the material. Hardness is essentially the resistance of the surface of
a material to deformation. There is no absolute scale for hardness,
each hardness form of test having its own scale. Though some
relationships exist betwen results on one scale and those on
another, care has to be taken in making comparisons because the
tests associated with the scales are measuring different things.

The most common form of hardness tests for metals involves
standard indentors being pressed into the surface of the material
concerned. Measurements associated with the indentation are then
taken as a measure of the hardness of the surface. The Brinell test,
the Vickers test and the Rockwell test are the main forms of such
tests.

With the *Brinell test* (*Figure 2.30*) a hardened steel ball is pressed
for a time of 10 to 15 s into the surface of the material by a standard
force. After the load and the ball have been removed the diameter

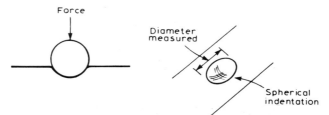

Figure 2.30   The basis of the Brinell hardness test

of the indentation is measured. The Brinell hardness number
(signified by HB) is obtained by dividing the size of the force
applied by the spherical surface area of the indentation. This area
can be obtained either by calculation or the use of tables, from the
values of the diameter of the ball used and the diameter of the
indentation.

$$\text{Brinell hardness number} = \frac{\text{applied force}}{\text{spherical surface area of indentation}}$$

The units used for the area are mm^2 and for the force are kgf (1 kgf =
9.8 N). The British Standard for this test is BS 240.

The diameter D of the ball used and the size of the applied force F
are chosen, for the British Standard, to give F/D^2 values of 1, 5, 10 or
30, the diameters of the balls being 1, 2, 5 or 10 mm. In principle, the
same value of F/D^{2-} will give the same hardness value, regardless of
the diameter of the ball used.

The Brinell test cannot be used with very soft or very hard
materials. In the one case the indentation becomes equal to the

diameter of the ball and in the other case there is either no or little indentation on which measurements can be based. The thickness of the material being tested should be at least ten times the depth of the indentation if the results are not to be affected by the thickness of the sample.

The *Vickers test* (*Figure 2.31*) uses a diamond indenter which is pressed for 10 to 15 s into the surface of the material under test. The result is a square-shaped impression. After the load and indenter

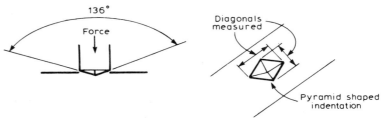

Figure 2.31   The basis of the Vickers hardness test

are removed the diagonals of the indentation are measured. The Vickers hardness number (HV) is obtained by dividing the size of the force applied by the surface area of the indentation. The surface area can be calculated, the indentation is assumed to be a right pyramid with a square base (the vertex angle of the pyramid is assumed to be the same as the vertex angle of the diamond, i.e 136°), or obtained by using tables and the diagonal values. The relevant British Standard is BS 427.

The Vickers test has the advantage over the Brinell test of the increased accuracy that is possible in determining the diagonals of a square as opposed to the diameter of a circle. Otherwise it has the same limitations as the Brinell test.

The *Rockwell test* (*Figure 2.32*) uses either a diamond cone or a hardened steel ball as the indenter. A force is applied to press the indenter in contact with the surface. A further force is then applied

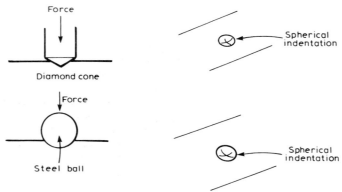

Figure 2.32 The basis of the Rockwell hardness test

and causes an increase in depth of the indenter penetration into the material. The additional force is then removed and there is some reduction in the depth of the indenter due to the deformation of the material not being entirely plastic. The difference in the final depth of the indenter and the initial depth, before the additional force was applied, is determined. This is the permanent increase in penetration (e) due to the additional force.

Rockwell hardness number (HR) = E–e

where E is a constant determined by the form of the indenter. For the diamond cone indenter, E is 100, for the steel ball, E is 130.

There are a number of Rockwell scales, the scale being determined by the indenter and the additional force used. The following table indicates the scales and the types of materials for which each are typically used.

Scale	Indenter	Additional force/kN	Typical applications
A	Diamond	0.59	Thin steel and shallow case-hardened steel.
B	Ball 1.588 mm dia.	0.98	Copper alloys, aluminium alloys, soft steels.
C	Diamond	1.47	Steel, hard cast irons, deep case-hardened steel.
D	Diamond	0.98	Thin steel and medium case-hardened steel.
E	Ball 3.175 mm dia.	0.98	Cast iron, aluminium alloys, magnesium alloys, bearing metals.
F	Ball 1.588 mm dia.	0.59	Annealed copper alloys, thin soft sheet metals, brass.
G	Ball 1.588 mm dia.	1.47	Malleable irons, gun metals, bronzes, copper-nickel alloys.
H	Ball 3.175 mm dia.	0.59	Aluminium, lead, zinc.
K	Ball 3.175 mm dia.	1.47	Aluminium and magnesium alloys.
L	Ball 6.350 mm dia.	0.59	Plastics.
M	Ball 6.350 mm dia.	0.98	Plastics.
P	Ball 6.350 mm dia.	1.47	
R	Ball 12.70 mm dia.	0.59	Plastics.
S	Ball 12.70 mm dia.	0.98	
V	Ball 12.70 mm dia.	1.47	

The relevant British Standard for Rockwell tests is BS 891. In any reference to the results of a Rockwell test the scale letter must be quoted. The B and C scales are probably the most commonly used for metals.

For the most commonly used indenters with the Rockwell test the size of the indentation is rather small. Localised variations of structure, composition and roughness can thus affect the results. The Rockwell test is however more suitable for workshop or 'on site' use as it is less affected by surface conditions than the Brinell or Vickers tests which require flat and polished surfaces to permit accurate measurements. The test, as indicated above, cannot be used with thin sheet. A variation of the standard test, called the *Rockwell superficial hardness test*, can be used however with thin sheet. Smaller forces are used and the depth of the indentation is determined with a more sensitive device as much smaller indentations are used. The initial force is 29.4 N instead of 90.8 N. The following are the scales given by this test.

Scale	Indenter	Additional force/kN
15–N	Diamond	0.14
30–N	Diamond	0.29
45–N	Diamond	0.44
15–T	Ball 1.588 mm dia.	0.14
30–T	Ball 1.588 mm dia.	0.29
45–T	Ball 1.588 mm dia.	0.44

Note: numbers with the scale letter refer to the additional force values when expressed in kgf units (1 kgf = 9.8 N).

COMPARISON OF THE DIFFERENT HARDNESS SCALES

The Brinell and Vickers tests both involve measurements of the surface areas of indentations; the form of the indenters however is different. The Rockwell tests involve measurements of the depths of penetration of the indenter. Thus the various tests are concerned with different forms of material deformation as an indication of hardness. There are no simple theoretical relationships between the various hardness scales though some approximate, experimentally derived, relationships have been obtained. Different relationships hold for different metals.

The following table shows the conversions that are used between the different tests for steels.

Brinell value	Vickers value	Rockwell values	
		B	C
112	114	66	
121	121	70	
131	137	74	
140	148.	78	
153	162	82	
166	175	86	4
174	182	88	7
183	192	90	9
192	202	92	12
202	213	94	14
210	222	96	17
228	240	98	20
248	248	102	24
262	263	103	26
285	287	105	30
302	305	107	32
321	327	108	34
341	350	109	36
370	392		40
390	412		42
410	435		44
431	459		46
452	485		48
475	510		50
500	545		52

Up to a hardness value of 300 the Vickers and Brinell values are almost identical.

There is an approximate relationship between hardness values and tensile strengths. Thus for annealed steels the tensile strength in $N\ mm^{-2}$ is about 3.54 times the Brinell hardness value, and for quenched and tempered steels 3.24 times the Brinell hardness value. For brass the factor is about 5.6, and for aluminium alloys about 4.2.

Example

An aluminium alloy (4.0% Cu, 0.8% Mg, 0.5% Si, 0.7% Mn) has a hardness of 45 HB when annealed and 100 HB when solution treated and precipitation hardened. What might be the tensile strengths of the alloys in these two conditions?

If the tensile strength is assumed to be the hardness value multiplied by 4.2 then the tensile strength in the annealed condition is $189\ N\ mm^{-2}$ and in the heat treated condition is $420\ N\ mm^{-2}$. The measured values were $180\ N\ mm^{-2}$ and $430\ N\ mm^{-2}$.

HARDNESS MEASUREMENTS WITH PLASTICS

The Brinell, Vickers and Rockwell tests can be used with plastics. The Rockwell test with its measurement of penetration depth rather than surface area of indentation is more widely used. Scale R is a commonly used scale, e.g. Nylon 6 (Durethan 30S) has a Rockwell hardness on scale R of 120.

The British Standard test (BS 2782) involves an indenter, a ball of diameter 2.38 mm, being pressed against the plastic by an initial force of 0.294 N for 5 s and then an additional force of 5.25 N being applied for 30 s. The difference between the two penetration depths is measured and expressed as a *softness number*. This is just the depth expressed in units of 0.01 mm. Thus a penetration of 0.05 mm is a softness number of 5. The test is carried out at a temperature of $23 \pm 1°C$.

Another form of this test is the *Shore durometer*. This involves an indenter in the form of either a truncated cone with a flat end or spherically-ended cone.

THE MOH SCALE OF HARDNESS

One form of hardness test is based on assessing the resistance of a material to being scratched. With the *Moh scale* ten materials are used to establish a scale. The materials are arranged so that each one will scratch the one preceding it in the scale but not the one that succeeds it. The following is the list of the materials in this scale.

1 Talc
2 Gypsum
3 Calcspar
4 Fluorspar
5 Apatite
6 Felspar
7 Quartz
8 Topax
9 Corundum
10 Diamond

Thus felspar will scratch apatite but not quartz. Diamond will scratch all the materials, while talc will scratch none of them.

Ten stylii of the materials in the scale are used for the test. The hardness number of a material under test is one number less than that of the substance that just scratches it. Thus, for instance, glass can just be scratched by felspar but not by apatite. The glass has thus a hardness number of 5.

TYPICAL HARDNESS VALUES

The following table gives typical hardness values for metals and plastics at room temperature.

Material	Hardness value
Aluminium, commercial, annealed	21 HB
hard	40 HB
Aluminium–1.25% Mn, alloy, annealed	30 HB
hard	30HB
Copper, oxygen-free HC, annealed	45 HB
hard	105 HB
Cartridge brass, 70% Cu, 30% Zn, annealed	65 HB
hard	185 HB
Magnesium alloy–6% A1, 1% Zn, 0.3% Mn, forged	65 HB
Nickel alloy, Monel, annealed	110 HB
cold worked	240 HB

Material	Hardness value
Titanium alloy–5% A1, 2.5% tin, annealed	360 HB
Zinc casting alloy A, as cast	83 HB
Grey cast iron	210 HB
White cast iron	400 HB
Malleable cast iron, Blackheart	130 HB
Carbon steel–0.2% carbon, normalised	150 HB
Stainless steel, austenitic (304), annealed	150 HB
cold worked	240 HB
PVC, no plasticiser	110 HRR
Polystyrene	80 HRM
ABS	70 HRM
Nylon 6	110 HRR

Figure 2.33 shows the general range of hardness values for the different types of materials when related to Vickers, Brinell, Rockwell and Moh hardness scales.

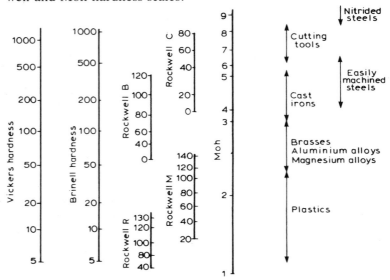

Figure 2.33 Hardness values

OTHER MECHANICAL TESTS

Compression testing is used with materials such as cast iron and concrete which might be used in service to resist compressive forces. Compression testing is just the opposite of tensile testing, the sample of material being compressed instead of stretched.

Engineering materials generally give a stress–strain graph which is approximately the same in the elastic region as that given by the tensile test. Thus, for instance, the tensile modulus and the compression modulus tend to be the same, since the slope of the stress–strain graph is generally the same in tension and compression.

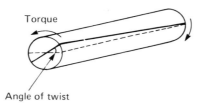

Figure 2.34 The principle of the torsion test

Another type of test is the torsion test. This involves applying a torque to a test sample and measuring the angle of twist (*Figure 2.34*). The results are then plotted as a graph or torque against angle of twist.

THERMAL CONDUCTIVITY

The following are some typical values of thermal conductivity. The higher the value of the conductivity, the greater is the rate at which heat will be transferred through a piece of the material of given size.

	Material	Thermal conductivity/W m^{-1} K^{-1}
Metals	Aluminium	230
	Copper	380
	Iron, cast	52
	Mild steel	54
	Stainless steel	16
Polymers	Bakelite	0.23
	Nylon (66)	0.025
	PVC	0.0019
Ceramics	Alumina	2
	Titanium carbide	3
	Glass	1
Composites	Concrete	1.4
	Wood	0.14
	Brick	0.83

The above values should only be considered as indicative of the types of values that might be encountered at normal ambient-temperatures. The values are much affected by impurities and by temperature.

If a component is required which is to conduct heat rapidly away from some hot body then a metal is indicated, copper being one of the best choices. If, however, an insulator is required then a composite or a polymer is indicated.

ELECTRICAL CONDUCTIVITY

The following are typical values, at about room temperature, of electrical conductivity. Values for electrical resistivity can be obtained from the data, since the resistivity is the reciprocal of the conductivity.

$$\text{Resistivity} = \frac{1}{\text{conductivity}}$$

Material		Conductivity/ ohm^{-1} m^{-1}
Metals	Aluminium	40,000
	Copper	64,000
	Iron	11,000
	Mild steel	6,600
Polymers	Acrylic	Less than 10^{-14}
	Nylon	10^{-9} to 10^{-14}
	PVC	10^{-13} to 10^{-14}
Ceramics	Alumina	10^{-10} to 10^{-13}
	Glass	10^{-10} to 10^{-12}
Composites	Wood	About 10^{-10}

Metals are good electrical conductors; polymers, ceramics and composites are generally insulators.

PROBLEMS

1 Explain the terms: tensile strength, tensile modulus, limit of proportionality, yield stress, proof stress, percentage elongation, percentage reduction in area.

2 Explain why tensile test pieces have a standard relationship between gauge length and cross-sectional area.

3 The following results were obtained from a tensile test of an aluminium alloy. The test specimen had a diameter of 11.28 mm and a gauge length of 56 mm. Determine (a) the stress-strain graph, (b) the tensile modulus, (c) the 0.1% proof stress.

Load/kN	0	2.5	5.0	7.5	10.0	12.5	15.0	17.5
Extension/10^{-2}mm	0	1.8	4.0	6.2	8.4	10.0	12.5	14.6

Load/kN	20.0	22.5	25.0	27.5	30.0	32.5	35.0
Extension/10^{-2}mm	16.3	19.0	21.2	23.5	25.7	28.1	31.5

Load/kN	37.5	38.5	39.0	39.0	(broke)
Extension/10^{-2}mm	35.0	40.0	61.0	86	

4 A flat tensile piece of steel had a gauge length of 100.0 mm. After fracture, the gauge length was 131.1 mm. What was the percentage elongation?

5 The following data was obtained from a tensile test on a stainless steel test piece. Determine (a) the limit of proportionality stress, (b) the tensile modulus, (c) the 0.2% proof stress.

Stress/N mm^{-2}	0	90	170	255	345	495	605
Strain/10^{-4}	0	5	10	15	20	30	40

Stress/N mm^{-2}	700	760	805	845	880	895
Strain/10^{-4}	50	60	70	80	90	100

6 Determine from the stress–strain graph for cast iron given in *Figure 2.6*, the tensile strength and the limit of proportionality.

7 Determine from the stress–strain graph for an aluminum alloy given in *Figure 2.7*, the tensile modulus.

8 What is meant by a 'proportional test piece'?

9 *Figure 2.35* shows part of the stress–strain graph for a sample of nylon 6. Estimate (a) the tensile modulus and (b) the tensile strength for the sample.

10 What is the secant modulus of elasticity?

11 What is the effect of strain rate on the data obtained from tensile tests for plastics?

12 Sketch the form of the stress–strain graphs for (a) brittle stiff materials, (b) brittle non-stiff materials, (c) ductile stiff materials, (d) ductile non-stiff materials.

13 The effect of working an aluminium alloy (1.25% manganese) is to change the tensile strength from 110 N mm^{-2} to 180 N m^{-2} and the percentage elongation from 30% to 3%. Is the effect of the working to (a) make the material stronger, (b) make the material more ductile?

14 A sand-cast aluminium alloy (12% silicon) is found to have a percentage elongation of 5%. Would you expect this material to be brittle or ductile?

15 An annealed titanium alloy has a tensile strength of 880 N mm^{-2} and a percentage elongation of 16%. A nickel alloy, also in the annealed condition, has a tensile strength of 700 N mm^{-2} and a percentage elongation of 35%. Which alloy is (a) the stronger, (b) the more ductile in the annealed condition?

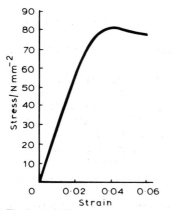

Figure 2.35 Part of the stress–strain graph for Nylon 6 (Durethan SK)

16 Cellulose acetate has a tensile modulus of 1.5 kN mm^{-2} while polythene has a tensile modulus of 0.6 kN mm^{-2}. Which of the two plastics will be the stiffer?

17 Describe the Izod or the Charpy impact test.

18 Describe the difference between the appearance of a brittle and a ductile fracture in an impact test piece.

19 Explain how impact tests can be used to determine whether a heat treatment process has been carried out successfully.

20 The following are Izod impact energies at different temperatures for samples of annealed cartridge brass (70% copper – 30% zinc). What can be deduced from the results?

Temperature/°C	+27	−78	−197
Impact energy/J	88	92	108

21 The following are Charpy V-notch impact energies for annealed titanium at different temperatures. What can be deduced from the results?

Temperature/°C	+27	−78	−196
Impact energy/J	24	19	15

22 The following are Charpy impact strengths for nylon 6.6 at different temperatures. What can be deduced from the results?

Temperature/°C	−23	−33	−43	−63
Impact strength/kJ m^{-2}	24	13	11	8

23 The impact strength of samples of nylon 6, at a temperature of 22°C, is found to be 3 kJ m^{-2} in the as moulded condition, but 25 kJ m^{-2} when the sample has gained 2.5% in weight through water absorption. What can be deduced from the results?

24 Describe a bend test and explain the significance of the results of such a test.

25 Describe the principles of the Brinell, Vickers and Rockwell hardness measurement methods.

26 How can a hardness measurement give an indication of the tensile strength of a material?

27 Outline the limitations of the Brinell hardness test.

28 With Rockwell test results, a letter A, B, C, etc. is always given with the results. What is the significance of the letter?

29 Which hardness test could be used with thin steel sheet?

30 Explain what is meant by the Moh scale of hardness.

31 A sample of brass can just be scratched by calcite but not by gypsum. What would be its Moh hardness number?

32 Specify the type of test that could be used in the following instances.

(a) A large casting is to be produced and a check is required as to whether the correct cooling rate occurs.

(b) The storekeeper has mixed up two batches of steel, one batch having been surface hardened and the other not. How could the two be distinguished?

(c) What test could be used to check whether tempering has been correctly carried out for a steel?

(d) A plastic is modified by the inclusion of glass fibres. What test can be used to determine whether this has made the plastic stiffer?

(e) What test could be used to determine whether a metal has been correctly heat treated?

(f) What test could be used to determine whether a metal is in a suitable condition for forming by bending?

33 Examine the following components and explain, in terms of electrical conductivity, the use of different materials for the various constituent parts.

(a) A mains electrical plug.

(b) A car sparking plug.

(c) The electrical cable used to connect an electrical appliance to the domestic mains supply.

34 If copper has an electrical conductivity of 64,000 ohm^{-1} m^{-1}, what is its resistivity?

35 Explain why a cold drinking-glass is liable to crack when a hot liquid is suddenly poured into it. In your answer use the terms thermal conductivity and thermal expansivity.

36 In selecting a cutting tool material, the thermal conductivity and thermal expansivity have to be considered, particularly if the material is brittle. Explain why this is so.

3 Basic structure of materials

Objectives   At the end of this chapter you should be able to:

- *Describe the three states of matter.*
- *Describe, in simple terms, the main types of bonding.*
- *Explain what is meant by the crystalline state.*
- *Recognise the simple cubic, face-centred cubic, body-centred cubic and close-packed hexagonal structure of crystals.*
- *Recognise that structure affects properties.*

ATOMS AND MOLECULES

All matter is made up of atoms. A material that is made up of just one type of atom is called an element. Hydrogen, carbon, copper and iron are examples of elements. An atom is the smallest particle of an element that has the characteristics of that element. We can thus talk of a copper atom or an iron atom. Atoms themselves are made up of other particles which are not characteristic of the element but are basic building blocks out of which all atoms are constructed. Each atom is composed of a nucleus, which is positively charged, and electrons, which are negatively charged. We can think of an atom as being a very small nucleus, which contains virtually all the mass of the atom, surrounded by a cloud of electrons which occupy most of the space of the atom (*Figure 3.1*). Some of the electrons can be considered to 'live' close to the nucleus and some near the 'edge' of the atom.

The term *molecule* is used to describe groups of atoms which tend to exist together in a stable form. Thus, for instance, hydrogen tends to exist in a stable form as a combination of two hydrogen atoms rather than as just individual atoms. Some molecules may exist as combinations of atoms from a number of dfferent elements. Water, for example, consists of molecules each of which is made up of two hydrogen atoms and an oxygen atom.

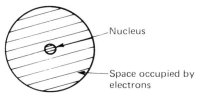

Figure 3.1 An idealised picture of an atom

Nucleus

Space occupied by electrons

STATES OF MATTER

Materials can be classified as having three possible states: gas, liquid or solid. Solids have definite shapes and volumes. Liquids have definite volumes but can alter their shape to take up the shape of a containing vessel. Gases have no definite volume or shape but expand until they fill any container in which they are placed.

Thus water can exist as ice (the solid form), as a liquid, or as steam (the gaseous form).

The definite shape of solids suggests that there are strong attractive forces between the constituent atoms or molecules, which pull them together, whereas in liquids the forces must be weaker since the shape can be so readily altered. In gases these forces must be very weak, or non-existent, since gases can assume any shape. Solids have, generally, higher densities than liquids, which in turn have higher densities than gases. This would suggest that, in gases, atoms (or molecules) are far apart, but that in liquids they are closer together and in solids even closer. What we are really saying is that the forces between atoms, or between molecules, depend on the distance separating them.

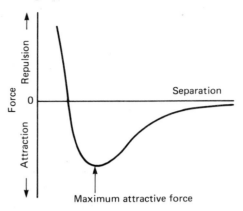

Figure 3.2

Figure 3.2 shows the basic form of a force-separation graph which we can use to describe the above behaviour. At large separations the force of attraction is very small. As the separation decreases the attractive force becomes larger, reaching a maximum at the separation which would be appropriate for the solid state. If we try to push atoms, or molecules, closer together than this separation, the force becomes repulsive. Without this repulsive force there would be nothing to stop the attractive forces pulling all the atoms, or molecules, closer and closer together until eventually all the matter vanished into a very small point.

BONDS   The way in which atoms join together, or molecules join together, is called bonding. The following are the different types of bonding that can occur; the type of bonding existing within a material determines many of its properties.

Transfer of electrons
An individual atom is electrically neutral, having as much positive charge as negative charge. However, if an atom loses an electron (a packet of negative charge), it ends up with a net positive charge. It is then referred to as an ion – in this case, a *positive ion*. If an atom gains an extra electron it ends up with a net negative charge, becoming a *negative ion*. In an ionically bonded material, an atom of one element gives an electron to an atom of another element. One element then consists of positive ions and the other of negative ions. Unlike charged bodies attract each other. Thus there is a force of attraction between the atoms of the two constituent elements in the material. Such a form of bonding is called *ionic bonding* (*Figure 3.3(a)*). Materials with this form of bonding have high melting and boiling points since the bond is a very strong one. Sodium chloride, common salt, is an example of a material with this form of bonding.

Sharing of electrons
Oxygen in the gaseous state consists of oxygen molecules made up

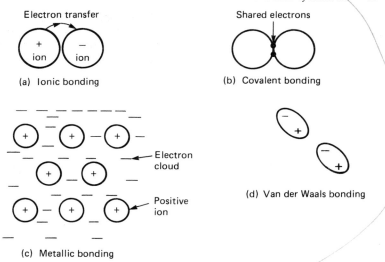

Figure 3.3 Types of bond

of two oxygen atoms. There is thus a bond between the two oxygen atoms. This form of bonding involves each atom donating an electron to form a pair of electrons which is shared between both atoms. We can, figuratively, think of there being two positive ions held together by a pair of electrons between them, each ion being attracted to the electrons. This particular form of bonding is called *covalent bonding (Figure 3.3(b))*.

Electron cloud
In a metal, such as copper, we have atoms losing electrons and becoming positive ions. The electrons that have been lost (in the case of copper, one electron is lost from each atom) do not combine with any one ion but remain as a cloud of negative charge floating between the ions. The result is bonding, this form of bonding often being referred to as *metallic bonding (Figure 3.3(c))* since it is characteristic of metals. The free electrons explain why metals are such good conductors of electricity.

Van der Waals bonding
If you rub a piece of plastic, perhaps a ballpoint pen against a piece of cloth, then it becomes electrically charged. If now this charged piece of plastic is brought near to a small piece of (uncharged) paper, the paper becomes attracted to the plastic. This is because the charge on the paper becomes redistributed as a result of the presence of the charged piece of plastic: the charge of the same sign as that on the plastic is repelled to the remoter parts of the paper, while that of a sign different from that on the plastic is attracted to the nearer part of the paper. The result is that there is a smaller distance between the unlike charges and a greater distance between the like charges. Like charges repel, unlike charges attract. The smaller distance between the unlike charges means that there is a net attractive force between the plastic and the paper. A similar effect can occur between two atoms or two molecules – the charge distribution in each can be distorted and so give rise to a weak attractive force. This force is called a *van der Waals force (Figure 3.3(d))*.

CRYSTALS   If someone refers to crystals you may well think of material which is geometrically regular in shape, perhaps like the cubes of common salt or sugar. Such crystals have smooth flat faces with the angle between adjoining faces always 90°. Some salt crystals may be small cubes, others large cubes or shapes involving effectively a number of cubes stuck together.

Figure 3.4 shows copper sulphate crystals growing in a drop of solution. Each crystal grows in a regular way, and maintains the same basic shape until it impinges on another crystal or some other obstacle.

The form of crystals and the way in which they grow can be explained if matter is considered to be made up of small particles which are packed together in a regular manner. *Figure 3.5* shows how a simple cube can be made by stacking four spheres. The cube can 'grow' if further spheres are added equally to all faces of the four-sphere-cube (*Figure 3.6*). The result is a bigger cube which can be considered to be made up of a larger number of the basic four-sphere-cube.

The dotted lines in *Figure 3.5* enclose what is called the *unit cell*. In this case the unit cell is a cube. The unit cell is the geometric figure which illustrates the grouping of the particles in the solid. This group is repeated many times in space within a crystal, which can be considered to be made up, in the case of a *simple cubic crystal*, of a large number of these unit cells stacked together. *Figure 3.7* shows that portion of the stacked spheres that is within the unit cell. The crystal is considered to consist of large numbers of particles arranged in a regular, repetitive pattern, known as the *space lattice*, as in *Figure 3.6*.

It is this regular, repetitive pattern of particles that characterises crystalline material. A solid having no such order in the arrangement of its constituent particles is said to be *amorphous*.

The simple cubic crystal shape is arrived at by stacking spheres in one particular way (*Figure 3.8 (a)*). By stacking spheres in different

Figure 3.4 Copper sulphate crystals growing from solution. (From Lewis, J., *Physics: 11–13,* Longman Group)

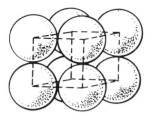

Figure 3.5 A simple cubic structure

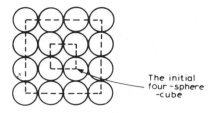

Figure 3.6 A two–dimensional view of the 'growing' four–sphere–cube

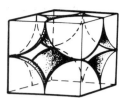

Figure 3.7 The simple cubic structure

ways, other crystal shapes can be produced (*Figure 3.8 (b) and (c)*). With the simple cubic unit cell the centres of the sphere lie at the corners of a cube. With the *body-centred cubic* unit cell the cell is slightly more complex than the simple cubic cell in having an extra sphere in the centre of the cell. The *face-centred cubic* cell is another modification of the simple cubic cell, having spheres at the centre of each face of the cube. Another common arrangement is the *hexagonal close-packed* structure.

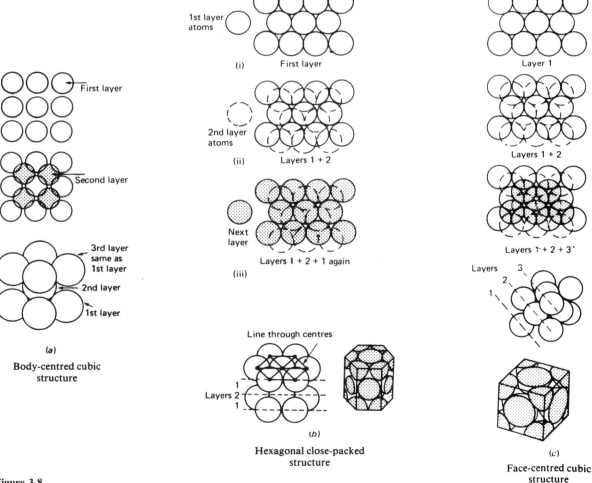

Figure 3.8

(a)

Body-centred cubic structure

(b)

Hexagonal close-packed structure

(c)

Face-centred cubic structure

STRUCTURE   The way in which atoms, or molecules, are packed together in a material is called the structure of that material. Sodium chloride – common salt – is composed of sodium ions, positive, and chlorine ions, negative. These are arranged in the simple cubic structure illustrated in *Figure 3.5*. A single crystal of sodium chloride, however, consists of large numbers of sodium and chlorine ions all bonded together in this cubic form into an enormous structure. *Figure 3.9* illustrates part of this structure. Such a structure is three-dimensional in the sense that ions are held in place by bonds in three dimensions.

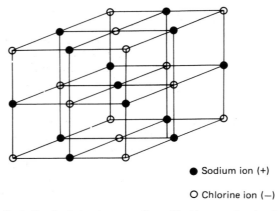

● Sodium ion (+)

○ Chlorine ion (−)

Figure 3.9 Part of a giant structure – sodium chloride crystal – showing the position of the ions

Diamond is an example of a crystal structure based solely on carbon atoms. Each atom is bound, by covalent bonding, to four other carbon atoms in a tetrahedral arrangement. *Figure 3.10* illustrates this arrangement and how an enormous three-dimensional structure can be built up. The strength of these bonds between the carbon atoms and the uniform arrangement in which each atom is held in its place in the structure makes diamond a very hard material.

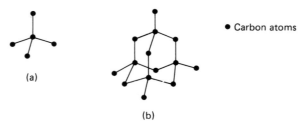

● Carbon atoms

(a)

(b)

Figure 3.10 (a) The bonding arrangement for the carbon atoms in diamond (b) Part of the three-dimensional structure of diamond

Graphite – the lead in pencils – is, by contrast, a very soft material. It is because layers of graphite can be easily removed that it finds a use as pencil lead. Graphite also, like diamond, consists only of carbon atoms. However, the way in which the carbon atoms are arranged in the solid is different and it is because of this difference that carbon has different properties in graphite and in diamond. *Figure 3.11* shows the structure of graphite. It can be considered to be a 'layered' structure since the atoms are strongly

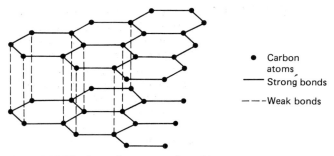

Figure 3.11 The layered structure of graphite

bonded together in two-dimensional layers, with only very weak bonds between the atoms in different layers.

The way in which atoms, or molecules, are packed together thus markedly affects the properties.

PROBLEMS

1 Describe the basic characteristics of the three states of matter.

2 Describe the basic types of bonding between atoms or molecules.

3 Explain the terms *unit cell* and *space lattice*.

4 How do differences of structure explain the different properties of diamond and graphite.

5 How does a crystalline material differ in structure from an amorphous material?

6 Explain how differences in the way ions are packed in a solid can lead to the different structure of simple cubic, face-centred cubic, body-centred cubic and close-packed hexagonal.

4 Structure of metals

Objectives   At the end of this chapter you should be able to:

- *Explain what alloys are.*
- *Distinguish between ferrous and non-ferrous alloys.*
- *Recognise the crystalline nature of metals.*

METALS AS CRYSTALLINE   Metals are crystalline substances. This may seem a strange statement in that metals do not generally seem to look like crystals, with their geometrically regular shapes. If the photograph of the growing copper sulphate crystals, *Figure 3.4*, had been taken a little later, it may well have been difficult to identify the regular shapes of the copper sulphate crystals. Indeed, near the bottom of the photograph the regularity of shape is not apparent. This is where the crystals in their growing have impinged on each other and prevented the individual crystals reaching their geometrically regular shapes. *Figure 4.1* shows a section of a metal. The surface looks much like the surface pattern that would have been produced with the growing copper sulphate crystals if the growth had continued until all the space had been filled.

CHILL CRYSTALS   COLUMNAR CRYSTALS

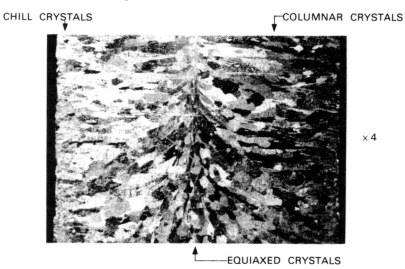

× 4

EQUIAXED CRYSTALS

Figure 4.1 Cross-section of a small aluminium ingot. (From Monks, H.A. and Rochester, D.C., *Technician Structure and Properties of Metals*, Cassell)

The term *grain* is used to describe the crystals within the metal. A grain is merely a crystal without its geometrical shape and flat faces because its growth was impeded by contact with other crystals. Within a grain the arrangement of particles is just as regular and repetitive as within a crystal with smooth faces. A simple model of a metal with its grains is given by the raft of bubbles on the surface of a

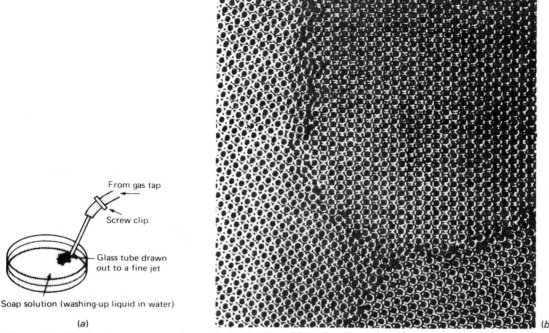

From gas tap

Screw clip

Glass tube drawn
out to a fine jet

Soap solution (washing-up liquid in water)

(a)   (b)

Figure 4.2 (a) Simple arrangement for producing bubbles, (b) 'grains' in a bubble raft. (Courtesy of the Royal Society)

liquid (*Figure 4.2*). The bubbles pack together in an orderly and repetitive manner but if 'growth' is started at a number of centres then 'grains' are produced. At the boundaries between the 'grains' the regular pattern breaks down as the pattern changes from the orderly pattern of one 'grain' to that of the next 'grain'.

The grains in the surface of a metal are not generally visible. They can be made visible by careful etching of the surface with a suitable chemical. The chemical preferentially attacks the grain boundaries.

Here are some examples of the different forms of crystal structure adopted by metallic elements.

Body-centred cubic	Face-centred cubic	Hexagonal close-packed
Chromium	Aluminium	Beryllium
Molybdenum	Copper	Cadmium
Niobium	Lead	Magnesium
Tungsten	Nickel	Zinc

GROWTH OF METAL CRYSTALS

Copper sulphate crystals growing in copper sulphate solution are shown in *Figure 3.4*. How do metal crystals grow in liquid metal? *Figure 4.3* shows the various stages that can occur when a metal solidifies. Crystallisation, whether with metals or the copper sulphate, occurs round small nuclei, which may be impurity particles. The initial crystals that form have the shape of the crystal pattern into which the metal normally solidifies, e.g. face-centred cubic in the case of copper. However, as the crystal grows it tends to develop

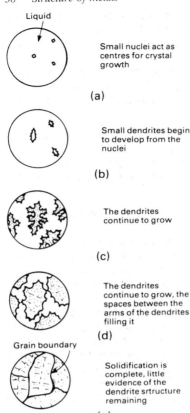

Liquid

Small nuclei act as centres for crystal growth

(a)

Small dendrites begin to develop from the nuclei

(b)

The dendrites continue to grow

(c)

The dendrites continue to grow, the spaces between the arms of the dendrites filling it

(d)

Grain boundary

Solidification is complete, little evidence of the dendrite srtructure remaining

(e)

Figure 4.3 Solidification of a metal

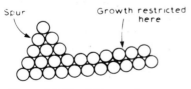

Spur   Growth restricted here

Figure 4.5 Dendritic growth

spikes. The shape of the growing crystal thus changes into a 'tree-like' growth called a *dendrite* (*Figure 4.4*). As the dendrite grows so the spaces between the arms of the dendrite fill up. Outward growth of the dendrites cease when the growing arms meet other dendrite arms. Eventually the entire liquid solidifies. When this happens there is little trace of the dendrite structure, only the grains into which the dendrites have grown.

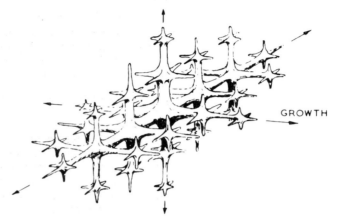

GROWTH

Figure 4.4 Growth of a metallic dendrite (From Higgins, R.A., *Properties of Engineering Materials*, Hodder & Stoughton)

Why do metals tend to grow from the melt as dendrites? Energy is needed to change a solid, at its melting point, to a liquid without any change in temperature occurring; this energy is called *latent heat*. Similarly, when a liquid at the fusion point (i.e. the melting point) changes to a solid, energy has to be removed, no change in temperature occurring during the change of state; this is the latent heat. Thus, when the liquid metal in the immediate vicinity of the metal crystal face solidifies, energy is released which warms up the liquid in front of that advancing crystal face. This slows, or stops, further growth in that direction. The result of this action is that spikes develop as the crystal grows in the directions in which the liquid is coolest. As these warm up in turn, so secondary, and then tertiary, spikes develop as the growth continues in those directions in which the liquid is coolest. This type of growth can be considered in terms of the 'crystal shapes' generated by stacking spheres in an orderly manner (*Figure 3.8*). Instead of stacking the spheres over the entire 'crystal' surface, the spheres are only stacked on parts of that surface (*Figure 4.5*). The result is that although the material is still growing into a crystal with the same unit cell arrangement the growth is not even in all directions; spurs develop.

STRUCTURE OF INGOTS AND CASTINGS

Ingots and castings involve the pouring of liquid metal into a mould; the term *ingots* is used if a simple block is produced for shaping with further processing, whereas with a *casting* no further major shaping is required. During the solidification the grains are produced. The shape and size of the grains depend in the main on the number of nuclei at which the grains start to grow and the direction and rate of crystal growth. These are influenced by the casting temperature, the mass of metal in the casting, the rate at which it cools and the composition of the metal. This is discussed in more detail in Chapter 5.

As the molten metal solidifies, it shrinks, so that the final solidified casting does not completely fill the mould which was originally full of liquid metal. This *shrinkage* occurs for the following reasons:

(a) the liquid metal contracts in cooling from its pouring temperature to the solidification temperature;

(b) on changing from liquid to solid, most metals contract;

(c) the solid contracts further in cooling from its solidification temperature to its final temperature.

Shrinkage may, however, cause cavities to form within the casting.

A casting may show *gas holes* formed by gas that is trapped in the metal during the casting process. This may be gas that is dissolved in the metal when it is in the liquid state, or it may be produced as a result of chemical reactions during solidification, or be generated from the mould walls during the casting.

A casting is generally not completely chemically homogeneous throughout. A molten metal can contain insoluble impurities, such as slag and dross. These result in *inclusions* within the solidified metal. A molten metal will also contain soluble impurities as well as soluble alloying elements. In the solidification process, the crystals that are first produced may contain different amounts of soluble elements from those that are produced later. This effect is known as *segregation*.

ALLOYS   Brass is an alloy composed of copper and zinc. Bronze is an alloy of copper and tin. An *alloy* is a metallic material consisting of an intimate association of two or more elements. The everyday metallic objects around you will be made almost invariably from alloys rather than the pure metals themselves. Pure metals do not always have the appropriate combination of properties needed; alloys can however be designed to have them.

The coins in your pocket are made of alloys. Coins need to be made of a relatively hard material which does not wear away rapidly, i.e. the coins have to have a 'life' of many years. Coins made of, say, pure copper would be very soft; not only would they suffer considerable wear but they would bend in your pocket.

Coins (British)	Percentage by mass			
	Copper	Tin	Zinc	Nickel
½p, 1p, 2p	97	0.5	2.5	–
5p, 10p, 50p	75	–	–	25

If you put sand in water, the sand does not react with the water but retains its identity, as does the water. The sand in water is said to be a mixture. In a *mixture*, each component retains its own physical structure and properties. Sodium is a very reactive substance, which has to be stored under oil to stop it interacting with the oxygen in the air, and chlorine is a poisonous gas. Yet when these two substances interact, the product, sodium chloride, is eaten by you and me every day. The product is common salt. Sodium chloride is a compound. In a *compound* the components have interacted and the product has none of the properties of its constituents. Alloys are generally mixtures though some of the components in the mixture may interact to give compounds as well.

IRON ALLOYS

Pure iron is a relatively soft material and is hardly of any commercial use in that state. Alloys of iron with carbon are however very widely used. The following table indicates the names given to general groups of such alloys.

Material	Percentage carbon
Wrought iron	0 to 0.05
Steel	0.05 to 2
Cast iron	2 to 4.3

The percentage of carbon alloyed with iron has a profound effect on the properties of the alloy. The term *carbon steel* is used for those steels in which essentially just iron and carbon are present. The term *alloy steel* is used where other elements are included. This chapter considers just the carbon steels.

PLAIN CARBON STEELS

Plain carbon steels are essentially just alloys of iron and carbon. Other elements are however invariably present in such steels, e.g. manganese, silicon, sulphur and phosphorus. The term *plain carbon steel* is however restricted to those steels where the carbon does not exceed 1.5%, the manganese about 1.5%, the silicon about 0.5% and the other elements are no more than traces. The mechanical properties of such steels are determined primarily by the percentage of carbon in the steel.

Plain carbon steels are often grouped into three categories. The term *mild steel* is used where the carbon content is between about

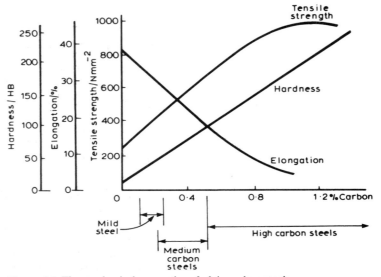

Figure 4.6 The mechanical properties of plain carbon steels

0.10 and 0.25%, *medium carbon steel* for between 0.20 and 0.50% carbon, and *high carbon steel* for between 0.5 and 1.5% carbon. *Figure 4.6* shows the effects of the carbon content on the mechanical properties of the steel. Increasing the carbon content increases the hardness and the tensile strength but decreases the elongation.

Mild steels have relatively low tensile strength and hardness but high ductility. Typical applications of mild steel are sections for use as joists in buildings, bodywork for cars and ships, screws, nails and wire. Medium carbon steels have higher tensile strength and hardness but lower ductility than mild steels. Typical applications are agricultural tools, fasteners, dynamo and motor shafts, crankshafts, connecting rods and gears. High carbon steels have the highest tensile strength and hardness but very low elongations. They are used where hardness is a more necessary requirement than ductility. Typical applications are tools, saws, hammers, chisels, punches, axes, dies, taps, drills and razors.

NON–FERROUS ALLOYS

The term *ferrous alloys* is used for those alloys having iron as the base element, e.g. cast iron and steel. The term *non-ferrous alloys* is used for those alloys which do not have iron as the base element, e.g. alloys of aluminium. The following are some of the non-ferrous alloys in common use in engineering:

Aluminium alloys | Aluminium alloys have a low density, good electrical and thermal conductivity, high corrosion resistance. Typical uses are metal boxes, cooking utensils, aircraft body-work and parts.

Copper alloys | Copper alloys have good electrical and thermal conductivity, high corrosion resistance. Typical uses are pump and valve parts, coins, instrument parts, springs, screws. The names brass and bronze are given to some forms of copper alloys.

Magnesium alloys | Magnesium alloys have a low density, good electrical and thermal conductivity. Typical uses are castings and forgings in the aircraft industry.

Nickel alloys | Nickel alloys have good electrical and thermal conductivity, high corrosion resistance, can be used at high temperatures. Typical uses are pipes and containers in the chemical industry where high resistance to corrosive atmospheres is required, food processing equipment, gas turbine parts. The names Monel, Inconel and Nimonic are given to some forms of nickel alloys.

Titanium alloys | Titanium alloys have a low density, high strength, high corrosion resistance, can be used at high temperatures. Typical uses are in aircraft for compressor discs, blades and casings, in chemical plant where high resistance to corrosive atmospheres is required.

Zinc alloys | Zinc alloys have good electrical and thermal conductivity, high corrosion resistance, low melting points. Typical uses are as car door handles, toys, car carburettor bodies – components that in general are produced by die casting.

Non-ferrous alloys have, in general, these advantages over ferrous alloys:

(a) good resistance to corrosion without special processes having to be carried out;

(b) most non-ferrous alloys have a much lower density and hence lighter weight components can be produced;

(c) casting is often easier because of the lower melting points;

(d) cold working processes are often easier because of the greater ductility;

(e) high thermal and electrical conductivities;
(f) more decorative colours.

Ferrous alloys have these advantages over non-ferrous alloys:

(a) generally greater strengths;
(b) generally stiffer materials, i.e. larger values of Young's modulus;
(c) better for welding.

PROBLEMS

1 Explain the term *grain*, when used in connection with a metal.

2 Describe the process of dendritic crystal growth in a metal.

3 Describe the origin of the solidification defects of shrinkage, gas holes, inclusions and segregation.

4 Explain how the grain structure of a metal surface can be seen and examined.

5 Explain what is meant by the term *alloy*.

6 Describe the essential differences in mechanical properties between mild steel and medium and high carbon steels, giving typical applications of these materials.

7 Explain the terms *ferrous alloy* and *non-ferrous alloy*.

8 What in general are the main differences in properties between ferrous and non-ferrous alloys?

5 Shaping metals

Objectives At the end of this chapter you should be able to:

- *Describe the effect of hot and cold work on a metal structure.*
- *Describe the effect of heat on cold worked metals.*
- *Describe the effect of grain size and shape on the mechanical properties of metals.*
- *Predict the type of grain structure, and hence mechanical properties, that will occur for given work and temperature conditions.*

PLASTIC DEFORMATION OF METALS

When a material is stretched beyond its elastic limit, plastic deformation can occur (see Chapter 2). With plastic deformation a material does not return to its original dimensions when the applied stress is removed but is permanently deformed. An important group of forming processes used with metals involves shaping the metals by plastic deformation. These processes include rolling, drawing, pressing, spinning, forging and extrusion.

What happens to a metal when plastic deformation occurs? Metals are crystalline. This means that the metal atoms are arranged in a regular manner within the crystal. This regular array of atoms enables us to consider the atoms in a crystal as lying in a number of planes (Figure 5.1). The different planes have different densities of

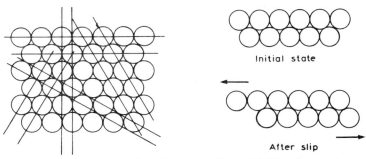

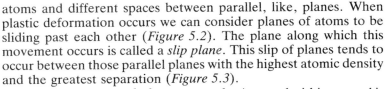

Figure 5.1 Some of the possible planes in a regularly packed array of atoms

Figure 5.2 Slip of atom planes

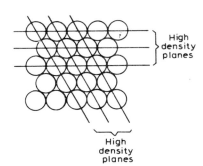

Figure 5.3

atoms and different spaces between parallel, like, planes. When plastic deformation occurs we can consider planes of atoms to be sliding past each other (*Figure 5.2*). The plane along which this movement occurs is called a *slip plane*. This slip of planes tends to occur between those parallel planes with the highest atomic density and the greatest separation (*Figure 5.3*).

Metals are composed of many crystals. A crystal within a metal is just a region of orderly packed atoms. Such a region is generally referred to as a *grain*. The surfaces that divide the different regions of orderly packed atoms are termed *grain boundaries*. When plastic deformation occurs in a metal, movement occurs along slip planes and the result is rather like *Figure 5.4*. Slip occurs only in those planes which are at suitable angles to the applied stress. The result is

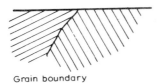

Grain boundary

Before the application of
stress
(a)

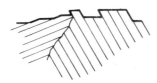

After plastic deformation
(b)

Figure 5.4 (a) Before the application of stress, (b) after plastic deformation

that the surface of the metal shows a series of steps due to the different movements of the various planes of atoms. These can be seen under a microscope (*Figure 5.5*). As will be seen from the figure the slip lines do not cross over from one grain to another; the grain boundaries restrict the slip to within a grain. Thus the bigger the grains the more slippage that can occur; this would show itself as a greater plastic deformation. A fine grain structure should therefore have less slippage and so show less plastic deformation, i.e. be less ductile. A brittle material is thus one in which each little slip process is confined to a short run in the metal and not allowed to spread, a ductile material is one in which the slip process is not confined to a short run and does spread over a large part of the metal.

Figure 5.5 Slip steps in polycrystalline aluminium. (The Open University TS 251/6, © 1973 The Open University Press)

COLD WORKING Suppose you were to take a carbon steel test piece and perform a tensile test on it. You may, for instance, find that the material showed a yield stress of 430 N mm^{-2}. If the test is continued beyond this point but the stress released before the tensile strength is reached a permanent deformation of the test piece will be found to have occurred. *Figure 5.6* illustrates this sequence of events. Suppose you now repeat the test. This time the yield stress is not 430 N mm^{-2} but 550 N mm^{-2}. The material has a much higher yield stress (*Figure 5.7*). This phenomena is called *cold working*.

It is not only the yield stress that changes during cold working and it is not only carbon steel that shows such changes. The term cold

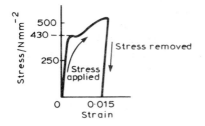

Figure 5.6

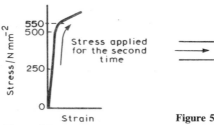

Figure 5.7

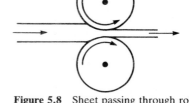

Figure 5.8 Sheet passing through rollers and being plastically deformed

working is applied to any process which results in plastic deformation at a temperature which does not alter the structural changes produced by the working. The following table shows some of the changes that take place when a sheet of annealed aluminium is rolled and its thickness reduced (*Figure 5.8*).

Reduction in sheet thickness %	Tensile strength /N mm^{-2}	Elongation %	Hardness HV
0	92	40	20
15	107	15	28
30	125	8	33
40	140	5	38
60	155	3	43

(Based on a table in John, V.B., *Introduction to Engineering Materials*, Macmillan)

As the amount of plastic deformation is increased so the tensile strength increases, the hardness increases and the elongation decreases. The material is becoming harder as a result of the cold working, hence the term sometimes applied to cold working of *work hardening*. The more the material is worked the harder it becomes. Also, as the percentage elongation results above indicate the more a material is worked the more brittle it becomes. A stage can however be reached when the strength and hardness are a maximum and the elongation a minimum and further plastic deformation is not possible, the material is too brittle. With the rolled aluminium sheet referred to in the above table, this condition has been reached with about a 60% reduction in sheet thickness. The material is then said to be *fully work hardened*.

Figure 5.9 shows how, for a number of materials, the hardness depends on the amount of cold working. The percentage reduction in thickness of a sheet or the percentage reduction in cross-sectional area of other forms of material is taken as a measure of the amount of working. As will be seen from the graph, as the amount of cold working increases the hardness increases until at some value of cold working a maximum hardness is reached. The material is then fully work hardened.

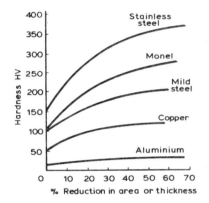

Figure 5.9 The effect of cold working on hardness

Example
Using *Figure 5.9*, what is the approximate percentage reduction in thickness of a sheet of mild steel that is possible before it becomes fully work hardened?

The mild steel would appear to have reached its maximum hardness with a percentage reduction in thickness of about 50 to 60%.

THE STRUCTURE OF COLD WORKED METALS

When stress is applied to a metal grain, deformation starts along the slip planes most suitably orientated. The effect of this is to cause the grains to become elongated and distorted. *Figure 5.10* shows the results of heavy rolling of a tin bronze ingot (4% tin). The grains have become elongated into fibre-like structures, which has the effect of giving the material different mechanical properties in different directions, a greater strength along the grain than at right angles to the grain. This effect can be used to advantage by the designer.

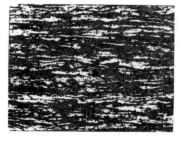

Figure 5.10 The grains in a heavily rolled tin bronze ingot. (From Rollason, E.C., *Metallurgy for Engineers*, Edward Arnold)

THE EFFECT OF HEAT ON COLD-WORKED METALS

Cold-worked metals generally have deformed grains and have often become rather brittle due to the working. In this process of deforming the grains, internal stresses build up.

When a cold-worked metal is heated to temperatures up to about $0.3\ T_m$, where T_m is the melting point of the metal concerned on the Kelvin scale of temperature, then the internal stresses start to become relieved. There are no changes in grain structure during this but just some slight rearrangement of atoms in order that the stresses become relieved. This process is known as *recovery*. Copper has a melting point of 1083°C, or 1356 K. Hence stress relief with copper requires heating to above about 407 K, i.e. 134°C.

If the heating is continued to a temperature of about 0.3 to $0.5\ T_m$ there is a very large change in hardness. The strength and also the structure of the metal change. The following table shows how the hardness of copper changes, the copper having been subject to a 30% cold working.

Temperature			Hardness HV
/°C	/K		
Initially			86
150	423	$(0.3\ T_m)$	85
200	473		80
250	523	$(0.4\ T_m)$	74
300	573		61
350	623	$(0.5\ T_m)$	46
450	723		24
600	873	$(0.6\ T_m)$	15

Figure 5.11 shows the above results graphically. Between $0.3\ T_m$ and $0.5\ T_m$ there is a very large change in hardness. The strength also decreases while the elongation increases. What is happening is that the metal is recrystallising.

With *recrystallisation* crystals begin to grow from nuclei in the most heavily deformed parts of the metal. The temperature at which recrystallisation just starts is called the *recrystallisation temperature*. This is, for pure metals, about 0.3 to $0.5\ T_m$.

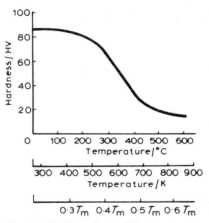

Figure 5.11 The effect of heat treatment on cold worked copper

Material	Melting point		Recrystallisation temperature		
	/°C	/K	/°C	/K	
Aluminium	660	933	150	423	$0.5\ T_m$
Copper	1083	1356	200	473	$0.3\ T_m$
Iron	1535	1808	450	723	$0.4\ T_m$
Nickel	1452	1725	620	893	$0.5\ T_m$

As the temperature is increased from the recrystallisation temperature so the crystals grow until they have completely replaced the original distorted cold worked structure. *Figure 5.12* illustrates this sequence and its relationship to the changes in physical properties.

The sequence of events that occur when a cold worked metal is heated can be broken down into three phases:

1 Recovery. The only significant change during this phase is the relief of internal stresses.

2 Recrystallisation. The hardness, tensile strength and percentage elongation all change noticeably during this phase.

3 Grain growth. The hardness, tensile strength and percentage elongation change little during this phase. The only change is that the grains grow and the material becomes large-grained.

During the *grain-growth* phase the newly-formed grains grow by

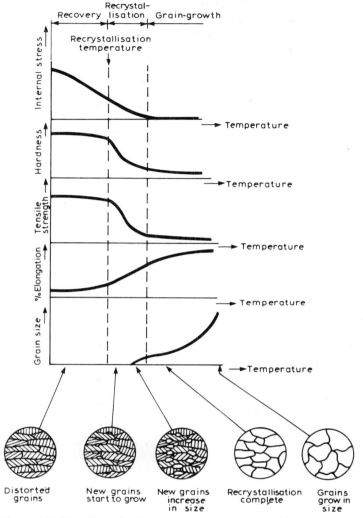

Figure 5.12 The effect of an increase in temperature on cold worked materials

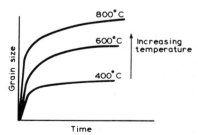

Figure 5.13 The effect of time and temperature on grain growth

absorbing other neighbouring grains. The amount of grain growth depends on the temperature and the time for which the material is at that temperature (*Figure 5.13*).

The term *annealing* is used for the heating process used to change the properties of a material. Thus, in the case of aluminium that has been cold worked and has become too brittle to work further, heating to above the recrystallisation temperature of 150°C enables new grains to grow and the material to become more ductile. The aluminium can then be worked further. This sequence of events, cold working followed by annealing and then further cold working, is used in many manufacturing processes.

Example
What is the minimum temperature at which recrystallisation occurs for cold worked copper?

The table on page 46 indicates the recrystallisation temperature as being 200°C for copper.

Example

A manufacturer of copper sheet receives the copper as much thicker plate, with already some amount of cold working. He proposes to produce the sheet by cold rolling in a number of stages, the stages being separated by annealing. Why is the sheet production in a number of stages?

If copper is cold-worked to about a 60% reduction in cross-sectional area it becomes brittle and tends to break with further working. Also at reductions approaching the 60% the material is becoming fairly hard and difficult to roll. By following rolling by annealing the material is made more ductile again and rolling can continue without difficulty.

FACTORS AFFECTING RECRYSTALLISATION

1 A minimum amount of deformation is necessary before recrystallisation can occur. The permanent deformation necessary depends on the metal concerned.

2 The greater the amount of cold work the lower the crystallisation temperature for a particular metal.

3 Alloying increases the recrystallisation temperature.

4 No recrystallisation takes place below the recrystallisation temperature. The higher the temperature above the recrystallisation temperature the shorter the time needed at that temperature for a given crystal condition to be attained.

5 The resulting grain size depends on the annealing temperature. The higher the temperature the larger the grain size.

6 The amount of cold work prior to the annealing affects the size of the grains. *Figure 5.14* shows the effect on the grain size of

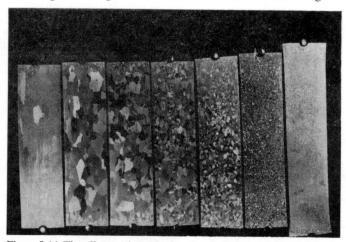

Figure 5.14 The effect on the grain size of annealing aluminium that has been subject to different amounts of cold work. Annealing involved, in all cases, 5 hours at 60°C. (From Rollason, E.C., *Metallurgy for Engineers,* Edward Arnold)

annealing aluminium that had been subject to different amounts of cold work. The greater the amount of cold work the smaller the resulting grain size. The greater the amount of cold work the more centres are produced for crystal growth.

HOT WORKING   Cold working involves plastically deforming materials below the recrystallisation temperature. The result is a harder, less ductile material with deformed grains. *Hot working* involves deforming a material at a temperature greater than the recrystallisation temperature. As soon as a grain becomes deformed it recrystallises, no hardening occurs and the working can be continued without any difficulty. No interruption of working is needed to anneal the material, as is the case with cold working.

The grain structure of hot-worked material depends on the temperature at which the working occurs, the type of working process involved and the cooling rate of the material after the hot working. If the temperature is just above the recrystallisation temperature a fine grain structure is produced, if it is well above this temperature then large grains will be produced.

A disadvantage of hot working is that oxidisation of the metal surfaces occurs; cold working does not have this problem. Another disadvantage is that the material will have comparatively low values of hardness and tensile strength, with high elongation. Hot and cold working processes are often both used in a particular shaping operation. The first operation involving large amounts of plastic deformation is carried out by hot working. After cleaning the material is then cold worked to increase the strength and hardness and give a good surface finish.

CAST AND WROUGHT PRODUCTS

Casting involves the shaping of a product by the pouring of liquid metal into a mould. The grain structure within the product is determined by the rate of cooling. Thus the metal in contact with the mould cools faster than that in the centre of the casting. This gives rise to small crystals, termed *chill crystals*, near the surfaces. These are smaller because the metal has cooled too rapidly for the crystals to grow to any size. The cooling rate nearer the centre is however much less and so some chill crystal can develop in an inward direction. This results in large elongated crystals perpendicular to the mould walls, these being called *columnar crystals*. In

CHILL CRYSTALS   ┌COLUMNAR CRYSTALS

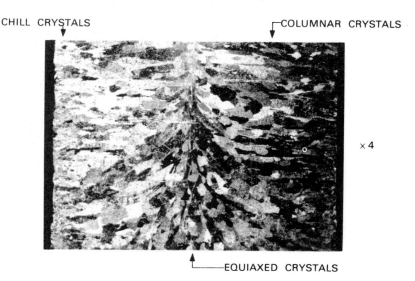

× 4

└─────EQUIAXED CRYSTALS

Figure 5.15 Grain structure in an aluminium casting. (From Monks, H.A. and Rochester, D.C., *Technician Structure and Properties of Metals2,* Cassell & Co.)

the centre of the mould the cooling rate is the lowest. While growth of the columnar crystals is taking place small crystals are growing in this central region. These grow in the liquid metal which is constantly on the move due to convection currents. The final result is a central region of medium-sized, almost spherical, crystals called *equiaxed crystals*. *Figure 5.15* shows all these types of crystals in a casting section.

In general a casting structure having entirely small equiaxed crystals is preferred. This type of structure can be promoted by a more rapid rate of cooling for the casting. Castings in which the mould is made of sand tend to have a slow cooling rate as sand has a low thermal conductivity. Thus sand castings tend to have large columnar grains and hence relatively low strength. Die casting involving metal moulds has a much faster rate of cooling and so gives castings having a bigger zone of equiaxed crystals. As these are smaller than columnar crystals the casting has better properties. The following table shows the types of differences that can occur with aluminium casting alloys.

Material	Tensile strength/N mm^{-2}		Percentage elongation	
	Sand cast	Die cast	Sand cast	Die cast
5% Si, 3% Cu	140	150	2	2
12% Si	160	185	5	7

Castings do not show directionality of properties, the properties being the same in all directions. They do however have the problems produced by working from a liquid metal of blowholes and other voids occurring during solidification.

Manipulative processes involve the shaping of a component by plastic deformation processes. The products given by such methods are said to be *wrought*. Hot working processes involve rolling, forging or extruding at temperatures in excess of the recrystallisation temperature. Cold working processes such as rolling, drawing, pressing, spinning and impact extrusion involve temperatures less than the recrystallisation temperature.

Rolling is a continuous process in which the material is passed between a pair of rotating rollers and emerges with a reduced thickness (as in *Figure 5.8*). Hot rolling is often at a temperature of about $0.6\ T_{m}$. At this temperature work hardening does not occur. The product is a relatively soft material with low tensile strength, the surfaces of the material are also oxidised. A ductile material can be cold rolled. Such a process work hardens the material and can lead to a useful gain in tensile strength and hardness. A good surface finish can be produced. Rolling does however give a directionality to the properties of the finished material due to the deformation of the grains in the direction of the rolling. The following table illustrates this for rolled brass strip (70% copper, 30% zinc).

Angle to rolling direction	Tensile strength /N mm^{-2}	Percentage elongation
0°	740	3
45°	770	3
90°	850	2

Forging involves squeezing a ductile material between a pair of dies. The term forging is generally only applied to the hot working process, though cold forging can be carried out with some of the very ductile non-ferrous materials. *Figure 5.16* shows the principle

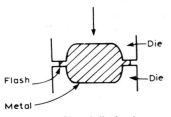

Figure 5.16 Closed-die forging

of one form of forging, closed-die forging. The flow of the material during the squeezing operation does give a directionality to the properties of the material.

Extrusion is rather similar to the squeezing of toothpaste out of the tube. The form of the ejected toothpaste is determined by the nozzle through which it is ejected. *Figure 5.17* shows the basic principles. Extrusion involves forcing a metal through a die. Hot extrusion involves temperatures of the order of $0.65 \ T_m$ to $0.9 \ T_m$. The result of hot extrusion is a product with comparatively low tensile strength and soft. Cold extrusion gives a cold-worked product with higher strength and hardness. The process is however possible where the cross-sectional area of the material is considerably reduced to too much work hardening occurring. The process of extrusion does give a product with directionality of properties.

In general, wrought products have a directionality of properties due to the process used giving rise to grain deformation in some particular direction.

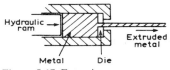

Figure 5.17 Extrusion

Example
Lead has a melting point of 327°C. Will the product be work hardened if lead is extruded at room temperature?

The melting point is about 600 K. This would mean that extrusion at about 300 K, about the order of room temperature is extrusion at about $0.5 \ T_m$. This just qualifies as a hot-working process. Thus the product should show no work hardening. The recrystallisation temperature is about the same as room temperature.

THE EFFECT OF GRAIN SIZE ON PROPERTIES

Grain size is an important factor in determining the mechanical properties of a material. It is not so much the size of the grain that is important as the length of grain boundary. Fine-grain material contains a greater length of grain boundaries than a coarse-grained material. Grain boundaries restrict the amount of slip that can occur in that slip within one grain is not easily transmitted across a grain boundary to cause slip in a neighbouring grain. Thus the more grain boundaries there are the more slip is restricted. Coarse-grained materials thus have lower yield stresses than fine-grained materials. This also means that a coarse-grained material will have a lower tensile strength than a fine-grained material. Hardness is related to tensile strength and thus coarse-grained material will have a lower hardness than fine-grained material. Ductile materials are those which have a large plastic region in their stress-strain relationship, thus we would expect the large-grain materials to be the more ductile as plastic deformation is easier.

The mechanical properties of a metal can be changed by changing the size or the shape of the grains. Cold-working distorts the shape of the grains and so increases tensile strength and hardness, while decreasing ductility. Annealing of a cold-worked material can increase ductility, while decreasing tensile strength and hardness, by reforming the grains without the distortion. It also enables the grain size to be controlled.

POWDER TECHNIQUES

Shaped metal components can be produced from a metal powder. The process, called *sintering*, involves compacting the powder in a die, then heating to a temperature high enough to knit together the particles in the powder. Sintering of tungsten takes place at about 1600°C, considerably below the melting point of 3410°C. The sintering temperature for iron is about 1100°C.

Sintering is a useful method for the production of components from brittle materials like tungsten or composite materials. Cobalt-bonded tungsten carbide tools are produced in this way. The method is useful also for high melting point materials for which the forming processes involving melting become expensive. The degree of porosity of the metal product can be controlled during the process, which is thus useful for the production of porous bronze bearings. The bearings are soaked in oil before use and can then continue in service for a considerable period of time.

PROBLEMS

1 Distinguish between cold- and hot-working processes.

2 Describe the effect on the mechanical properties of a metal of cold working.

3 Explain what is meant by the recrystallisation temperature.

4 What is meant by 'work-hardening'?

5 What are the properties of a fully work hardened material in comparison with its properties before any working occurs?

6 How does cold working change the structure of a metal?

7 Describe how the mechanical properties of a cold-worked material change as its temperature is raised from room temperature to about $0.6\ T_m$, where T_m is the melting point temperature in degrees Kelvin.

8 What factors affect the recrystallisation temperature of a metal?

9 How is the recrystallisation temperature of a pure metal related to its melting point?

10 Zinc has a melting point of 419°C. Estimate the recrystallisation temperature for zinc.

11 Magnesium has a melting point of 651°C. What order of temperatures would be required to (a) stress relieve, (b) anneal a cold-worked piece of magnesium?

12 What is the effect on the grain size of a metal after annealing of the amount of cold work the material had originally been subject to?

13 How does the temperature at which hot working is carried out determine the grain size and so the mechanical properties?

14 Describe the grain structure of a typical casting.

15 Why are the properties of a material dependent on whether it is sand-cast or die-cast?

16 What is meant by directionality in wrought products?

17 Why are the mechanical properties of a rolled metal different in the direction of rolling from those at right-angles to this direction?

18 How does a cold-rolled product differ from a hot-rolled product

19 Brasses have recrystallisation temperatures of the order of 400°C. Roughly what temperature should be used for hot extrusion of brass?

20 Describe how grain size and shape affect the mechanical properties of a metal.

21 A brass, 65% copper and 35% zinc, has a recrystallisation temperature of 300°C after having been cold-worked so that the cross-sectional area has been reduced by 40%.

(a) How will further cold working change the structure and the properties of the brass?

(b) To what temperature should the brass be heated to give stress relief?

(c) To what temperature should the brass be heated to anneal it and give a relatively small grain size?

(d) How would the grain size, and the mechanical properties change if the annealing temperature used for (c) was exceeded by 100°C?

22 Use *Figure 5.9* for this question.

(a) What is the maximum hardness possible with cold rolled copper?

(b) Copper plate, already cold worked 10% is further cold worked 20%. By approximately how much will the hardness change?

(c) Mild steel is to be rolled to give thin sheet. This involves a 70% reduction in sheet thickness. What treatment would be suitable to give this reduction and a final product which was no harder than 150 HV?

23 As a fine-grained product is generally desirable after some process, it is common to lower the temperature of a hot-working process to a working temperature just above the recrystallisation temperature for the final part of the process. Why should this lead to fine grains?

6 Polymers

Objectives At the end of this chapter you should be able to:

- *Describe the basic structural features of thermoplastic, thermosetting and elastomer materials, relating the mechanical and thermal properties to the structures.*
- *Describe the properties of common plastics, relating the properties to their structures.*

POLYMER STRUCTURE

The plastic washing-up bowl, the plastic measuring rule, the plastic cup – these are examples of polymeric materials. The molecules in these plastics are very large molecules. A molecule of oxygen consists of just two oxygen atoms joined together. A molecule in the plastic may have thousands of atoms all joined together in a long chain. The backbones of these long molecules are chains of carbon atoms. Carbon atoms are able to form strong bonds with themselves and produce long chains of carbon atoms to which other atoms can become attached.

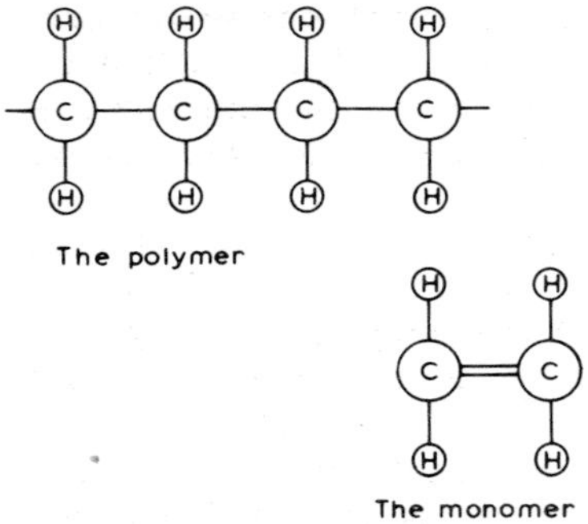

The term *polymer* is used to indicate that a compound consists of many repeating structural units. The prefix 'poly' means many. Each structural unit in the compound is called a *monomer*. Thus the plastic polyethylene is a polymer which has as its monomer the substance ethylene. For many plastics the monomer can be determined by deleting the prefix 'poly' from the name of the polymer. *Figure 6.1* shows the basic form of a polymer.

If you apply heat to the plastic washing up bowl the material softens. Removal of the heat causes the material to harden again. Such a material is said to be *thermoplastic* The term implies that the material becomes 'plastic' when heat is applied.

If you applied heat to a plastic cup you might well find that the material did not soften but charred and decomposed. Such a material is said to be *thermosetting plastic*.

Another type of polymer is the elastomers. Rubber is an elastomer. An *elastomer* is a polymer which by its structure allows considerable extensions which are reversible.

The thermoplastic, thermosetting and elastomer materials can be distinguished by their behaviour when forces are applied to them to cause stretching. Thermoplastic materials are generally flexible and relatively soft; if heated they become softer and more flexible. Thermosetting materials are rigid and hard with little change with an increase in temperature. Elastomers can be stretched to many times their initial length and still spring back to their original length when released. These different types of behaviours of polymers can be explained in terms of differences in the ways the long molecular chains are arranged inside the material.

Figure 6.2 shows some of the forms the molecular chains can take. These forms can be described as linear, branched and cross-linked. The linear chains have no side branches or chains or cross links with

The polymer

The monomer

Figure 6.1 The polymer, polyethylene

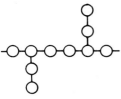

Linear polymer chain
(a)

Branched polymer chain
(b)

Cross-linked polymer
(c)

Figure 6.2 (a) Linear polymer chain, (b) branched polymer chain, (c) cross-lined polymer

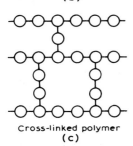

Figure 6.3 A linear amorphous polymer. Individual atoms are not shown, the chains being represented by lines

other chains. Linear chains can move readily past each other. If however the chain has branches there is a reduction in the ease with which chains can move past each other. This shows itself in the material being more rigid and having a higher strength. If there are cross-links a much more rigid material is produced in that the chains cannot slide past each other at all.

Polyethylene, a thermoplastic material, has linear molecular chains (in the high density version). Polyethylene is easily stretched and is not rigid. Because the chains are independent of each other they can easily flow past each other and so the material has a relatively low melting point, no energy being needed to break bonds between chains. The absence of bonds between chains also means that as none are broken when the material is heated the removal of heat allows the material to revert to its initial harder state.

Some thermoplastic materials have molecules with side branches; the effect of these is to give a harder and more rigid material. Polypropylene is such a material, being harder and more rigid than polyethylene. Another consequence of a material having branched chains is that, as they do not pack so readily together in the material as linear chains, the material will generally have a lower density than the linear chain material.

Thermosetting materials are cross-linked polymers and are rigid. As energy is needed to break bonds, before flow can occur, thermosetting materials have higher melting points than thermoplastic materials having linear or branched chains. Also the effect of heat is not reversible; when heat causes bonds to break an irreversible change to the structure of the material is produced. Bakelite is an example of a thermosetting material. It can withstand temperatures up to 200°C, but most thermoplastics are not used above 100°C.

Elastomers have linear molecular chains. In the material these chains are all tangled up and there is no order in the packing of the molecular chains in the material. These tangled chains give a relatively open structure with the large amount of empty space between the tangled chains. When forces are applied to the material the chains are able to move very easily within the voids. It is this which accounts for the very high extensions possible with elastomers.

CRYSTALLINITY IN POLYMERS

A crystalline structure is one in which there is an orderly arrangement of particles (see Chapter 3). A structure in which the arrangement is completely random is said to be *amorphous*. Many polymers are amorphous, the molecules in the material are completely randomly arranged. Highly cross-linked polymers (as in *Figure 6.2(c)*) are invariably armorphous. Linear polymers (*Figure 6.2(a)*) can be amorphous. *Figure 6.3* shows the type of structure that might occur for such a structure, the linear polymer chains being all tangled up.

Linear polymer chains can however assume an arrangement which is orderly. *Figure 6.4* shows the type of arrangement of chains that can occur, the linear chains folding backwards and forwards on themselves. The arrangement is said to be *crystalline*. The tendency of a polymer to crystallise is determined by the form of the polymer chains. Linear polymers can crystallise to quite an extent, complete crystallisation is not however obtained in that there are invariably some regions of disorder. Polyethylene can occur as linear chains

Figure 6.4 Folded linear polymer chains

and in this form can have a crystallinity as high as 95%, i.e. of the entire piece of polyethylene, 95% of the material will have an orderly structure. Polymers with side chains show less tendency to crystallise. Thus the branched form of polyethylene may only give 50% crystallinity. Cross-linked polymers have zero crystallinity.

Crystallinity in polymers affects the properties of the polymers. Linear polyethylene with 95% crystallinity has a density of about 950 kg m^{-3} and a melting point of 135°C. Branched polyethylene with 50% crystallinity has a density of about 920 kg m^{-3} and a melting point of 115°C. The greater the crystallinity the greater the density, i.e. the more closely packed the molecules can be. The two forms of polyethylene are often known as high density and low density polyethylene. Also the greater the crystallinity the higher the melting point, i.e. the more closely packed the molecules, the stronger the forces between them and so the greater the energy that has to be supplied to separate the molecules and melt the polymer.

Crystallinity also lowers the solubility of polymers in solvents. It does however lead to stiffer, stronger materials (i.e. higher tensile modulus and tensile strength).

PLASTICS   The term *plastics* is commonly used to describe materials based on polymers, i.e. long chain structures or networks. Such materials invariably contain other substances which are added to the polymers to give the required properties. Stabilisers, plasticisers and fillers are additives that are used. The term plastic is also restricted to those polymeric materials that are not elastomers.

Some plastics are damaged by ultraviolet radiation. Thus the effect of protracted periods of sunlight can lead to a deterioration of mechanical properties as well as a reduction in transparency or change in colour. An ultraviolet absorber is thus often added to plastics, carbon black being often used. Such an additive is called a *stabiliser*.

The term *plasticiser* is used for the material added to a polymer to make it more flexible. In one form the plasticiser may be liquid that is introduced after the polymer chains have been produced. The liquid disperses through the solid, filling up the spaces between the chains. The effect of this is the same as having a lubricant between two metal surfaces, so the polymer chains slide more easily past each other. One of the problems with such plasticised polymers is that the plasticiser can move out of the material with time. The vinyl upholstery used for car seats can lose its plasticiser and become more brittle. On a hot day the vinyl may feel greasy because of the plasticiser having migrated to the surface.

Another form of plasticisation involves replacing some of the links in the polymer chains by molecules which can more easily be deformed and so permit the chains to slide past each other more easily. Flexibility is thus increased.

The properties and the cost of a plastic can be markedly affected by the addition of other substances, these being termed *fillers*. The following table shows some of the common fillers used and their effects on the properties of the plastic.

Where the filler improves the tensile strength it generally does so by reducing the mobility of the polymer chains. An important consideration however in the use of any filler is the fact that the fillers are generally cheaper than the polymer and thus reduce the

Filler	Effect on properties
Asbestos	Improves temperature resistance, i.e. the plastic does not deform until a higher temperature is attained. Decreases strength and rigidity.
Cotton flock	Increases impact strength but reduces electrical properties and water resistance
Cellulose fibres	Increases tensile strength and impact strength
Glass fibres	Increases tensile strength but lowers ductility. Makes the plastic stiffer.
Mica	Improves electrical resistance
Graphite	Reduces friction
Wood flour	Increases tensile strength but reduces water resistance

overall cost of the plastic. Often up to 80% of a plastic may be filler.

One form of additive used is a gas. The result is foamed or 'expanded' plastics. Expanded polystyrene is used as a lightweight packing material. Polyurethanes in the expanded form are used as the filling for upholstery and as sponges.

COMMON PLASTICS *Polyethylene*, commonly known as *polythene*, is made in two forms (*Figure 6.5*) low-density or high density. Low-density polythene is essentially a linear chain polymer with a small number of branches. The effect of this is that only limited crystallisation is possible. This results in a lower density than if complete crystallisation had been possible, hence the term 'low-density' applied to this form of polythene. High-density polythene is a completely linear polythene

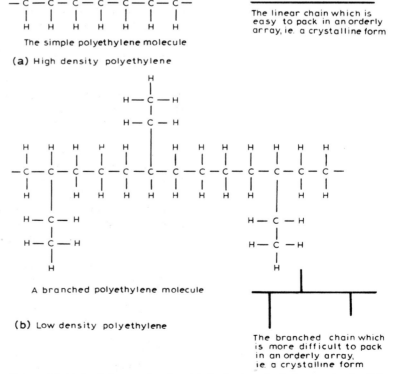

Figure 6.5 Polyethylene molecules, (a) the basic polyethylene molecule, (b) a branched polyethylene molecule

and a high degree of crystallisation is possible, resulting in the higher density.

The following table gives a comparison of the typical properties of these two forms of polythene.

Property	Low density	High density
Density/10^3 kg m^{-3}	0.92	0.95
Melting point / °C	115	135
Tensile strength/N mm^{-2}	8–16	22–38
Elongation %	100–600	50–800
Maximum service temp. / °C	85	125

Low-density polythene softens in boiling water, the high-density does not. Both forms are thermoplastics. Low-density polythene is used mainly in the form of films and sheeting, e.g. polythene bags, 'squeeze' bottles, ball-point pen tubing, wire and cable insulation. High-density polythene is used for piping, toys, filaments for fabrics and household ware. Both forms of polythene have excellent chemical resistance, low moisture absorption and high electrical resistance.

Low- and high-density polythene can be blended to give a material with properties between those of the two separate forms. The additives commonly used with polythene are carbon black as a stabiliser, pigments to give coloured forms, glass fibres to give increased strength and butyl rubber to prevent inservice cracking.

Polyvinyl chloride, commonly known as PVC, is a linear chain polymer with bulky side groups and so gives a mainly amorphous material (*Figure 6.6*). When used without a plasticiser it is a rigid,

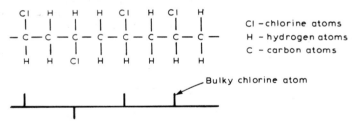

Figure 6.6 The basic form of a PVC molecule. The chlorine atoms are generally arranged irregularly on the different sides of the chain, so rendering orderly packing of the chains difficult

relatively hard material. Most PVC products are made with a plasticiser incorporated with the polymer. The amount of plasticiser is chosen to give a plastic with the required degree of flexibility, the amount varying between about 5 and 50%. Fillers, stabilisers and pigments are also often added.

The following table shows how the amount of plasticiser affects the properties of the PVC.

Property	No plasticiser content	Low plasticiser content	High plasticiser content
Density/10^3 kg m^{-3}	1.4	1.3	1.2
Tensile strength/N mm^{-2}	52–58	28–42	14–21
Elongation %	2–40	200–250	350–450
Maximum service temp./°C	70	60–100	60–100

The rigid form of PVC is used widely for piping, but not for hot water, as it has a maximum service temperature of only 70°C. Above that temperature it softens too much. Plasticised PVC is used for the fabric of 'plastic' raincoats, bottles, shoe soles, garden hose piping, gaskets and inflatable toys. All forms of PVC have good chemical resistance, though not as good as polythene. It is a thermoplastic.

Polystyrene has bulky side groups attached irregularly to the polymer chain and so gives an amorphous structure, as it is not possible to pack such chains together in an orderly manner. A form can be produced which has the side groups arranged more uniformly to give a crystalline structure, it is however not generally used commercially. Polystyrene with no additives is a brittle, transparent, material with a maximum service temperature of only about 65°C (the crystalline form has much better temperature properties with a melting point of 273°C). This type of polystyrene finds its main uses as containers for cosmetics, light fittings, toys and boxes.

A toughened polystyrene can be produced by blending polystyrene with rubber particles. This gives a marked improvement in properties, the material being much less brittle. This material has a considerable number of uses, e.g. cups used in vending machines, casings for cameras, projectors, radios, television sets and vacuum cleaners.

Another very useful material can be produced by forming the polymer chains with three different polymer materials, polystyrene, acrylonitrile and butadiene. The product is called *acrylonitrile – butadiene – styrene terpolymer*, or just *ABS*. This material is tough, stiff and resists abrasion. It is used as the casing for telephones, vacuum cleaners, hair driers, radios, typewriters, etc., as well as for safety helmets, luggage, boat shells and food containers.

The following table shows typical properties of these various forms of polystyrene.

Property	Polystyrene	Toughened polystyrene	ABS
Density/10^3 kg m^{-3}	1.1	1.1	1.1
Tensile strength/N mm^{-2}	35–60	17–42	17–58
Elongation %	1–3	8–50	10–140
Maximum service temp./°C	65	75	110

The above are all thermoplastic, amorphous materials. Polystyrene has good chemical resistance though can be attacked by some cleaning fluids. ABS has better chemical resistance.

Another widely used form of polystyrene is *expanded polystyrene*, which finds use as rigid air-filled structure for insulation and packaging.

Polyamides, or *nylons* as they are more commonly called, are linear polymers and give rise to crystalline structures. There are a number of common polyamides: nylon 6, nylon 6.6, nylon 6.10 and nylon 11. The numbers refer to the number of carbon atoms in each of the substances reacted together to give the polymer. The full stops separating the two numbers are sometimes omitted, e.g. nylon 66 is nylon 6.6. Nylon materials are strong, tough, and abrasion resistant. They are thermoplastic materials with a relatively high softening temperature. Nylons tend to absorb moisture, this reducing the strength. Though they have reasonable chemical resistance there are some chemicals that attack nylon.

The following table shows the properties that are obtained with common nylons.

Property	Nylon 6	Nylon 6.6	Nylon 6.10	Nylon 11
Density/10^3 kg m^{-3}	1.1	1.1	1.1	1.1
Tensile strength/N mm^{-2}	70–90	80	60	50
Elongation %	60–300	60–300	85–230	70–300
Maximum service temp./°C	120	120	120	120

The effect of water absorbed by the nylon can be a reduction in the tensile strength of about 30 to 50%.

Nylons often contain additives; a stabiliser may be used for a nylon which is exposed to ultraviolet radiation. Flame retardant additives may be used for nylon components exposed to fire risk. Glass spheres or glass fibres may be added to give improved strength and rigidity. The following table shows the effects on nylon 6 of such additives:

Property	50% glass spheres	30% glass fibres
Tensile strength/N mm^{-2}	75	155
Elongation %	4	6

The glass-fibre-filled nylon has also much better elevated temperature properties, a maximum service temperature of 180°C being possible.

Nylon is used for the manufacture of fibres for use in clothing. Gears and bearings are made from nylon, with its low frictional and self-lubricating properties. Molybdenum disulphide is used as an additive with Nylon 6 to give a material with very low frictional properties. Glass-sphere or glass-fibre-filled nylon is used for the housings of power tools, formers for electrical coils, electric plugs and sockets. Nylon is used for motor car door handles, lock components, fans, bushes and bearings.

THE GENERAL PROPERTIES OF PLASTICS

Compared with metals, plastics have a low density, of the order of 0.9 to 1.4×10^3 kg m^{-3}. Filled plastics may have higher densities, while expanded plastics will have lower densities. Unlike metals, they have low thermal and electrical conductivities. They are thus widely used where electrical insulators are required, e.g. the casing of electrical plugs or the sleeving for electrical wires. Plastics are considerably less stiff and have lower tensile strengths than metals. Fibre-filled plastics can however have high strengths and stiffnesses. Plastics have a low hardness, being much more easily indented than metals. The mechanical properties of plastics deteriorate rapidly with an increase in temperature, many plastics being of no use at temperatures above about 100°C. Some plastics are transparent, but coloured forms can be produced by the addition of pigments. Plastics are reasonably resistant to water and acids but can often be damaged by organic solvents, the reverse of the resistance of metals which are prone to damage by acids but not usually by organic solvents.

The cost per unit mass of plastics, with no additives, is higher than that of some metals. On the basis of cost per unit volume they are comparable with that of metals. One of the important cost factors is, however, the much lower manufacturing costs associated with plastics. The following relative costs are based on that of unit mass of aluminium.

Material	Relative cost per unit mass	Relative cost per unit volume
Aluminium	1	0.4
Polythene, low-density	0.4	0.4
Polythene, high-density	0.5	0.5
PVC	0.5	0.4
Polystyrene	0.5	0.5
ABS	1	1
Nylon	2	2

The following is an example of the information given by a manufacturer of plastics. (Courtesy of Bayer (UK) Ltd.)

Novodur (ABS polymer)

Appearance	Opaque, full gloss surface
Basic components	Acrylonitrile, butadiene, styrene
Physical structure	Amorphous
Density	1.03–1.06 Mg/m^3 compact
	0.3–1.0 Mg/m^3 expanded
Form supplied	Cubic granules
Bulk weight	500–600 g/1
Colour range	Available in natural colour and in all common opaque colours
Temperature performance	Maximum permanent service temperature without load:
	80–105°C, according to type
Processing methods	Processing the raw material:
	Injection moulding, extrusion, compression moulding, extrusion blow moulding, foam moulding and extruding.
	Processing the semi-fabricated form:
	Thermoforming, e.g. vacuum forming, cold forming, e.g. deep drawing
	Machining:
	Sawing, drilling, turning, milling, tapping, die-cutting
	Jointing:
	Non-detachable: cementing, welding, nailing, riveting
	Detachable: clamping and snap fitting, screwing
	Decorating:
	Painting, printing, metallising, embossing, polishing
Predominant applications	Domestic appliances, the automotive sector, radios, television and audio equipment, furniture, office equipment, still and ciné photography, electrical goods, toys, equipment for leisure activities, and the textile industry

ELASTOMERS

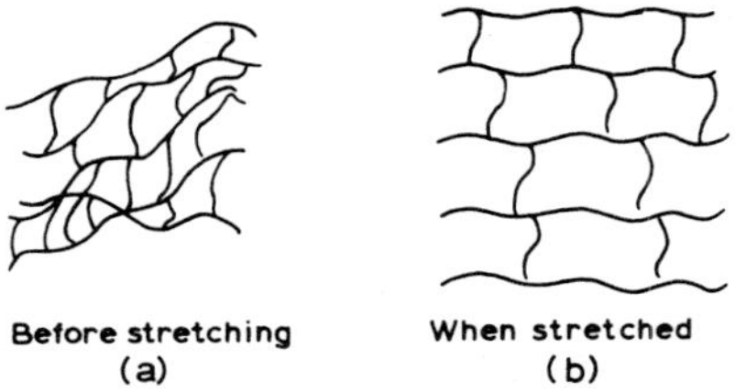

Before stretching (a)   When stretched (b)

Figure 6.7 Stretching an elastomer which has crossed links

Natural rubber is obtained from the sap of a particular type of tree. Both natural and synthetic rubbers are combined with additives such as plasticisers, anti-oxidants and fillers to give the required product. The products consist of linear chain molecules with some cross-linking between chains (*Figure 6.7*). This cross-linking is needed to ensure that the material will be elastic, i.e. return to its original dimensions when the load is removed. However, if there is too much cross-linking the material becomes less flexible and possibly even rigid. The introduction of sulphur into rubber to produce cross-links is called *vulcanisation*. Fully vulcanised rubber is the material known as *ebonite*.

The following table gives some of the properties of typical rubbers.

Material	Tensile strength /N mm^{-2}	Elongation /%	Service temp. range/°C
Natural rubber	30	800	−50 to +80
Butyl rubber	20	900	−50 to +100
Neoprene	25	1000	−50 to +100
Nitrile	28	700	−50 to +120
Silicone rubber	6	250	−80 to +235

Natural rubber and butyl rubber have relatively poor resistance to oils and greases. Silicone rubber has better resistance but neoprene and nitrile have very good resistance.

PROBLEMS

1 Distinguish between thermoplastic, thermosetting and elastomer materials on the basis of their elastic behaviour.

2 How does the behaviour of thermoplastic and thermosetting materials differ when they are heated?

3 Describe the difference between amorphous and crystalline polymer structures and explain how the amount of crystallinity affects the mechanical properties of the polymer.

4 Compare the properties of low- and high-density polythene and explain the differences in terms of structural differences between the two forms.

5 Why are (a) stabilisers, (b) plasticisers and (c) fillers added to polymers?

6 Describe how the properties of PVC depend on the amount of plasticiser present in the plastic?

7 Which form of PVC (i.e. without plasticiser, with a small amount or with a high amount) would be most likely to be used for the following applications.

   (a) Drain pipes.
   (b) Garden hose piping.
   (c) An inflatable toy.
   (d) A drinks bottle.

8 What is the effect on the properties of nylon of adding glass fibres?

9 How do the properties of plastics compare with those of metals?

10 Increasing the amount of sulphur in a rubber increases the amount of cross-linking between the molecular chains. How does this change the properties of the rubber?

11 A domestic bucket is to be made from polythene. Should high or low density polythene be used? Explain your answer.

12 Explain how elastomers can be stretched to several times their length and still be elastic and return to their original length.

7 Shaping non-metallic materials

Objectives At the end of this chapter you should be able to:

- *Distinguish the six main categories of polymer forming, i.e. extrusion, moulding, casting, calendering, forming and machining, and describe the types of product formed.*
- *Describe the forming processes that are most commonly used with ceramics.*

THE MAIN POLYMER-FORMING PROCESSES

Many polymer-forming processes are essentially two stage, the first stage being the production of the polymer in a powder, granule or sheet form and the second stage being the shaping of this material into the required shape. The first stage can involve the mixing with the polymer of suitable additives and even other polymers in order that the finished material should have the required properties. The additives may be in the form of solids, liquids or gases. Thus solid additives such as cork dust, paper pulp, chalk or carbon black are added to thermosetting polymers to reduce the brittleness of the material. Liquid additives may be used to improve the flow characteristics of the material during processing. Gas additives enable foamed or expanded materials to be produced.

Second-stage processes generally involve heating the powder, granule or sheet material until it softens, shaping the softened material to the required shape and then cooling it. The main types of process are:

1 Extrusion
2 Moulding
3 Casting
4 Calendering
5 Forming
6 Machining

The choice of process will depend on a number of factors, such as:

1 The quantity of items required.
2 The size of the items.
3 The rate at which the items are to be produced.
4 The requirements for holes, inserts, enclosed volumes, threads.
5 The type of material being used.

Items required in a continuous length are generally extruded while items required in large quantities, particularly small items, are generally moulded, the injection moulding process being used. Casting and forming are relatively slow processes, unlike injection moulding which is much faster. Calendering is used for the production of sheet plastic. Forming involves the shaping of sheet plastic.

Thermoplastic materials can be softened and resoftened indefinitely by the application of heat, provided the temperature is not so high as to cause decomposition. Because they flow readily with the application of heat they are particularly suitable for processing by extrusion and injection moulding; they can also be readily formed. Polyethylene, polyvinyl chloride, polystyrene, polyamide (nylon), polycarbonate, cellulose acetate and polytetra-fluoroethylene are examples of thermoplastics.

Thermosetting materials undergo a chemical change when they are subject to heat which cannot be changed by further heating. Moulding and casting are processes often used with such materials. Typical thermosetting resins are phenol formaldehyde, ureaformal-dehyde, melamine formaldehyde, unsaturated polyesters and epoxides.

The properties of the material can be affected markedly by the inclusion of gas, to give foamed plastics. Thus, for example, the thermoplastic material polyvinyl chloride can be made into a flexible foam material for use, perhaps, as cushioning material. Polystyrene foam is used for thermal insulation. Thermosetting materials can also be used to give foamed plastics.

Another way of altering the properties of the material is to include reinforcement material within it, usually in the form of fibres. A thermoplastic or thermosetting material with, perhaps, glass fibres within it is likely to be stronger and stiffer than the plastic on its own. If the fibres are all aligned in one direction the strength and stiffness in that direction will be markedly different from that in a direction at right angles to it. Glass fibres reinforced thermoplastic materials, e.g. nylon, is generally shaped by injection moulding.

EXTRUSION

Extrusion involves the forcing of the molten polymer through a die. The process is comparable with the squeezing of toothpaste out of its tube. *Figure 7.1* shows the basic form of the extrusion process. The polymer is fed into a screw mechanism which takes the polymer through a heated zone and forces it out through the die. In the case

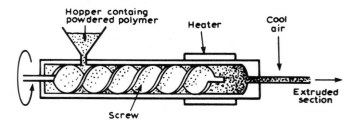

Figure 7.1   Extrusion

of an extruded product such as curtain rail the product is obtained by just cooling the extruded material. If thin film or sheet is the required product, a die may be used which gives an extruded cylinder of material. This cylinder while still hot is inflated by compressed air to give a sleeve of thin film. Another way of obtaining film or sheet is to use a slit die and cool the extruded product by allowing it to fall vertically into some cooling system.

The extrusion process can be used with most thermoplastics and yields continuous lengths of product. Intricate shapes can be produced and a high output rate is possible. Curtain rails, household guttering, polythene bags and film are examples of typical products.

Extrusion blow moulding is a process used widely for the production of hollow articles such as plastic bottles. Containers from as small as 10^{-6} m^3 to 2 m^3 can be produced. The process involves the extrusion of a hollow thick-walled tube which is then clamped in a mould. Pressure is applied to the inside of the tube, which inflates to fill the mould.

MOULDING

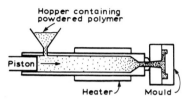

Hopper containing powdered polymer

Piston

Heater   Mould

Figure 7.2 Injection moulding by a ram-fed machine. Screw-fed machines as in *Figure 7.1* are also used

A widely used process for thermoplastics is *injection moulding*. With this process the polymer is melted and then forced into a mould (*Figure 7.2*). High production rates can be achieved and complex shapes with inserts, threads, holes, etc. can be produced. The process is particularly useful for small components. Typical products are beer or milk bottle crates, toys, control knobs for electrical equipment, tool handles, pipe fittings.

Foam plastic components can be produced by this method. Inert gases are dissolved in the molten polymer. When the hot polymer cools the gases come out of solution and expand to form a cellular structure. A solid skin is produced where the molten plastic comes in contact initially with the cold mould surface.

Widely used processes for thermosetting plastics are *compression moulding* and *transfer moulding*. In compression moulding, the powdered polymer is compressed between the two parts of the mould and heated under this pressure (*Figure 7.3*). With transfer moulding, the powdered polymer is heated in a chamber before being transferred by a plunger into the mould (*Figure 7.4*).

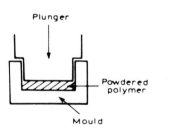

Plunger

Powdered polymer

Mould

Figure 7.3 Compression moulding

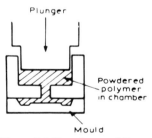

Plunger

Powdered polymer in chamber

Mould

Figure 7.4 Transfer moulding

CASTING

One form of casting involves mixing substances of relatively short molecular chains, with any required additives, in a mould so that polymerisation, i.e. the production of long-chain molecules, occurs during solidification. The term *cold-setting* is used generally for such polymers. Such methods are used for encapsulating small electrical components.

Reinforcement of cold-setting polymers can be produced by incorporating fibres, e.g. glass fibres, within the polymer. *Hand lay-up techniques* can be used with fibre-glass mats and cold-setting polymers. The process involves coating a mould with a non-stick coating. A glass-fibre mat is then spread by hand over the surface of the mould and the liquid mixture is spread over the mat. Further layers of mat and mixture can be added until the required thickness of material has been produced. Then time is allowed for the reaction to proceed, i.e. the long chain molecule chains to be produced, and hardening occurs. This type of technique is used by the many car owners when repairing rust or other damage to the metal bodywork of their cars. The technique has been used to produce entire car bodies.

Powder casting involves the melting of powdered polymer inside a heated mould. The mould is often rotated during this operation and the term *rotational moulding* used to describe the process. It is a very useful process for the production of hollow articles. This process does however have a slow rate of production. Powder casting can be used to coat surfaces with films of polymer, e.g. non-stick surfaces of cooking pans.

CALENDERING

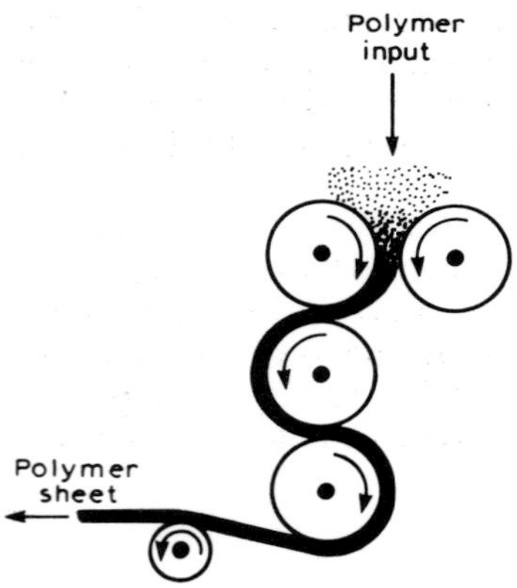

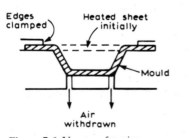

Figure 7.7 Calendering

Calendering is a process used for the production of continuous lengths of sheet thermoplastic, such as PVC or polythene. The calender consists of essentially three or more heated rollers (*Figure 7.5*). The heated polymer is fed into the gap between the first pair of rollers, emerging as a sheet. The group of rollers determines the rate at which the sheet is produced, the thickness of the sheet and the surface finish.

FORMING

Forming processes are used to mould articles from sheet polymer. The heated sheet is pressed into or around a mould. The term *thermoforming* is often used to describe this type of process. The sheet may be pressed against the mould by the application of air under pressure to one side of the sheet, *pressure forming*, or by the production of a drop in pressure, a vacuum, between the sheet and the mould, *vacuum forming* (*Figure 7.6*).

Thermoforming can have a high output rate, but dimensional accuracy is not too good and holes, threads, etc. cannot be produced. The method can be used for the production of large shaped objects but not very small items. Enclosed hollow shapes cannot be produced

Figure 7.6 Vacuum forming

MACHINING

While polymers can be machined by most of the methods commonly used with metals, the process used to shape the polymers often produces the finished article with no further need of machining or any other process. Polymers tend to have low melting points and thus correct machining conditions, which do not result in high temperatures being produced, are vital if the material is not to soften and deform. Some polymer materials are brittle and so present problems in machining, shock loadings having to be avoided if cracking is not to occur.

FORMING PROCESSES WITH CERAMICS

In general, the method used to form ceramics is to mould the material to the required shape and then heat it in order to develop the bonding between the particles in the material. As most ceramics are both hard and brittle the shape produced has generally to be the final shape as machining or cold working methods cannot be used.

A method used for the forming of clay shapes is *slip casting*. A suspension of clay in water is poured into a porous mould. Water is absorbed by the walls of the mould and so the suspension immediately adjacent to the mould walls turns into a soft solid. When a sufficient layer has built up, the remaining suspension is poured out, leaving a hollow clay object which is then removed from the mould and fired. This method is used for the production of wash basins and other sanitary ware.

The shaping of the block of wet clay on the potter's wheel is an example of *wet plastic forming*, the plastic clay mass being shaped by a tool before being fired. Another example of this type of forming is the extrusion of the plastic clay through dies, the extruded shape then being cut into appropriate lengths before being fired.

The *sintering* process, as described in Chapter 5 for metals, is used with ceramics. A version of this used with silicon involves compacting the silicon powder in an atmosphere of nitrogen at a temperature of about 1400°C. During the sintering process the silicon is converted into silicon nitride. This type of process is known as *reaction sintering* as it involves a chemical reaction as well as the sintering process.

PROBLEMS

1 State a process that could be used for the production of the following products:
   (a) plastic guttering for house roofs,
   (b) plastic bags,
   (c) the plastic tubing for ball-point pens,
   (d) plastic rulers,
   (e) a small, lightweight, plastic toy train,
   (f) a plastic tea cup and saucer,
   (g) the plastic body for a camera,
   (h) a hollow plastic container for liquids,
   (i) coating a metal surface with a coloured layer of polymer for decorative purposes,
   (j) a plastic milk bottle.

2 Describe the types of product produced by the following polymer processes:
   (a) extrusion,
   (b) injection moulding,
   (c) calendering,
   (d) thermoforming,
   (e) casting,

3 Describe the properties and some typical uses of foamed plastics.

4 Spectacle frames can be moulded from thermoplastic cellulose esters. Explain the process that would have been followed.

5 Why are plastic curtain rails made by extrusion rather than any other process?

6 What types of process are used with thermosetting materials?

7 The following is part of an advertisement by Wokingham Plastics Ltd. What types of product could be produced by the firm? Would there be any point, on the basis of the advertisement, in contacting them if you wanted someone to manufacture small toy railway engines?

'The case for vacuum forming is a case for Wokingham Plastics.

If it's plastic components you want – because they're tough, colourful, rust-free and inexpensive – contact Wokingham Plastics. We specialise. We have the necessary experience to form and fabricate industrial and domestic products. Such as fridge liners, car fascia panels, baths and showers, cravan interiors, light fittings. We work up to 2 m × 1 m, so virtually anything you need, we can make – in Polystyrene, ABS, PVC, Acrylic, CAB, Polycarbonate or Polypropylene.'

8 Composites

Objectives   At the end of this chapter you should be able to:

- *Give examples of common composites met in engineering.*
- *Explain how the mechanical properties of composites are related to fibre direction and properties of the matrix and fibre.*

EXAMPLES OF COMPOSITES

The term *composite* is used for a material composed of two different materials bonded together with one serving as the matrix surrounding fibres or particles of the other. A common example of a composite is reinforced concrete. This has steel rods embedded in the concrete (*Figure 8.1*). The composite enables loads to be carried

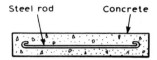

Figure 8.1 Reinforced concrete, steel rods in a matrix

Figure 8.2 Concrete aggregate in a matrix

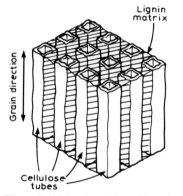

Figure 8.3 Wood, cellulose fibres in a lignin matrix

that otherwise could not have been carried by the concrete alone. Concrete itself is a composite, without the presence of steel reinforcement. It is made by mixing cement, sand, aggregrate and water. Stone chips or gravel are often used as the aggregate. The resulting concrete consists of the aggregate in a matrix (*Figure 8.2*).

There are many examples of composite materials encountered in everyday components. Many plastics are glass fibre or glass particle reinforced. Vehicle tyres are rubber reinforced with woven cords. Wood is a natural composite material with tubes of cellulose bonded by a natural plastic called lignin (*Figure 8.3*). Cermets, widely used for cutting tool tips, are composites involving ceramic particles in a metal matrix.

CONTINUOUS FIBRES IN A MATRIX

Consider a composite rod made up of continuous fibres, all parallel to the rod axis, in a matrix (*Figure 8.4*). These could be glass fibres in a plastic or steel reinforcement rods in concrete. Each element in the composite has a share of the applied force, thus

Total force = force on fibres + force on matrix

But the stress on the fibres is equal to force on them divided by their cross-sectional area. Similarly the stress on the matrix is equal to the force on the matrix divided by its area. Hence

Total force = stress on fibres × area of fibres + stress on matrix × area of matrix

Dividing both sides of the equation by the total area of the composite gives

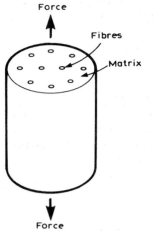

Figure 8.4 Continuous fibres in a matrix

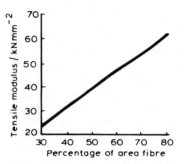

Figure 8.5 The effect of the percentage of cross-sectional area of glass fibre on the tensile modulus of a glass fibre-polyester composite

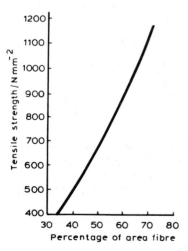

Figure 8.6 The effect of the percentage of cross-sectional area of glass fibre on the tensile strength of a glass fibre-polyester composite

$$\frac{\text{Total force}}{\text{total area}} = \text{stress on fibres} \times \frac{\text{area of fibres}}{\text{total area}} +$$

$$\text{stress on matrix} \times \frac{\text{area of matrix}}{\text{total area}}$$

The fraction of the cross-sectional area that is fibre is given by the area of the fibres divided by the total area, similarly the fraction of the cross-section that is matrix is the area of the matrix divided by the total area. The total area divided by the total force is the stress applied to the composite. Thus

Stress on composite = stress on fibres × area fraction fibres + stress on matrix × area fraction matrix

If the fibres are firmly bonded to the matrix then the elongation of contraction of the fibres and matrix must be the same and equal to that of the composite as a whole. Thus

Strain on composite = strain on fibres = strain on matrix

Dividing both sides of the stress equation by the strain gives an equation in terms of the tensile modulii (stress/strain = tensile modulus). Thus

Modulus of composite = modulus of fibres × area fraction fibres + modulus of matrix × area fraction matrix

Suppose we have glass fibres with a tensile modulus of 76 kN mm^{-2} in a matrix of polyester having a tensile modulus of 3 kN mm^{-2}. Then, if the fibres occupy 60% of the cross-sectional area, the tensile modulus of the composite will be given by

Modulus of composite = 76 × 0.6 + 3 × 0.4

= 46.8 kN mm^{-2}

The composite has a tensile modulus considerably greater than that of the polyester.

Not only has the composite a higher tensile modulus but also a higher strength than that of the matrix material. Thus for the 60% glass fibres in polyester the tensile strength may be about 800 N mm^{-2} for the composite when the matrix has a tensile strength of only about 50 N mm^{-2}.

For glass fibre-polyester composites with long fibres all in the same direction and all parallel to the axis of the composite along which the force is applied. *Figure 8.5* shows how the tensile modulus depends on the percentage of the area occupied by the fibres and *Figure 8.6* how the tensile strength is affected by this factor. Such composites usually have between 40% and 80% of the cross-sectional area as glass fibre. The following is the data for the glass fibres and polyester when separate.

	Tensile modulus /kN mm^{-2}	Tensile strength /N mm^{-2}
Polyester	2 to 4	20 to 70
E-glass fibres	76	1200 to 1800

Example

A column of reinforced concrete has steel reinforcing rods running through the entire length of the column and parallel to the column axis. If the concrete has a modulus of elasticity of 20 kN mm^{-2} and the steel 210 kN mm^{-2}, and the steel rods occupy 10% of the cross-sectional area of the column, what is the modulus of elasticity for the composite?

$$\text{Modulus of composite} = 210 \times 0.1 + 20 \times 0.9$$

$$= 39 \text{ kN mm}^{-2}$$

Example

Carbon fibres with a tensile modulus of 400 kN mm^{-2} are used to reinforce aluminium with a tensile modulus of 70 kN mm^{-2}. If the fibres are long and parallel to the axis along which the load is applied, and occupy 50% of the cross-sectional area of the composite, what is the tensile modulus of the composite?

$$\text{Modulus of composite} = 400 \times 0.5 + 70 \times 0.5$$

$$= 235 \text{ kN mm}^{-2}$$

REINFORCED PLASTICS

Reinforced plastics consist of a stiff, strong, material combined with the plastic. Glass fibres are probably the most used additive. The fibres may be long lengths, running through the length of the composite, or discontinuous short lengths randomly orientated within the composite. Another form of composite uses glass fibre mats or cloth in the plastic. The effect of the additives is to increase both the tensile strength and the tensile modulus of the plastic, the amount of change depending on both the form the additive takes and the amount of it. The continuous fibres give the highest tensile modulus and tensile strength composite but with a high directionality of properties. The strength along the direction of the fibres could be perhaps 800 N mm^{-2} while that at right-angles to the fibre direction may be as low as 30 N mm^{-2}, i.e. just about the strength of the plastic alone. Random orientated short fibres do not lead to this directionality of properties but do not give such high strength and tensile modulus. The composites with glass fibre mats or cloth tend to give tensile strength and modulus values intermediate between those of the continuous and short length fibres. The following are examples of the strength and modulus values obtained with reinforced polyester.

Material	Percentage weight of glass	Tensile modulus /kN mm^{-2}	Tensile strength /N mm^{-2}
Polyester	0	2 to 4	20 to 70
With short fibres	10 to 45	5 to 14	40 to 180
With plain weave cloth	45 to 65	10 to 20	250 to 350
With long fibres	50 to 80	20 to 50	400 to 1200

DISPERSION STRENGTHENED METALS

The strength of a metal can be increased by small particles dispersed throughout it. Thus solution treatment followed by precipitation hardening for an aluminium-copper alloy can lead to a fine dispersion of an aluminium-copper compound throughout the alloy. The result is a higher tensile strength material.

Aluminium alloy	Condition	Tensile strength /N mm^{-2}
4.0% Cu, 0.8% Mg 0.5% Si, 0.7% Mn	Annealed	190
	Solution treated, precipitation hardened	430

Another way of introducing a dispersion of small particles throughout a metal involves *sintering*. This process involves compacting a powdered metal powder in a die and then heating it to a temperature high enough to knit together the particles in the powder. If this is done with aluminium the result is a fine dispersion of aluminium oxide (about 10%) throughout an aluminium matrix. The aluminium oxide occurs because aluminium in the presence of oxygen is coated with aluminium oxide. When the aluminium powder is compacted, much of the surface oxide film becomes separated from the aluminium and becomes a fine powder dispersed throughout the metal. The aluminium oxide powder, a ceramic, dispersed throughout the aluminium matrix gives a stronger material than that which would have been given by the aluminium alone. At room temperature the tensile strength of the sintered aluminium powder is about 400 N mm^{-2}, compared with that of about 90 N mm^{-2} for commercial, annealed, aluminium. The sintered aluminium has an advantage over the precipitation hardened aluminium alloy in that it retains its strength better at high temperatures (*Figure 8.7*). This is because, at the higher temperatures, the precipitate particles tend to coalesce or go into solution in the metal.

Other dispersion-strengthened metals involving ceramics, have been developed. Thorium oxide particles (about 7%) in nickel give a composite which has good strength properties at high temperatures.

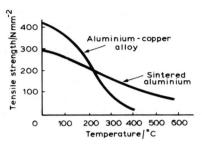

Figure 8.7 The effect of temperature on the tensile strength of an aluminium-copper alloy and sintered aluminium

CERMETS

Cermets are composites involving ceramics in a matrix of metal. The ceramics used have high strengths, high values of tensile modulus, high hardness, but are by themselves brittle substances. By comparison, the metals are weaker and less stiff, but they are ductile. By combining the ceramic with the metal, up to 80% ceramic, a composite can be produced which is strong, hard and tough. The composite has the ceramic in particle form in the metal matrix.

Typical ceramics used in cermets are carbides (tungsten, titanium, silicon, molybdenum), borides (chromium, titanium, molybdenum) and oxides (aluminium, chromium, magnesium), the metals being cobalt, chromium, nickel, iron or tungsten. A typical cermet used for cutting tool bits involves tungsten carbide in a matrix of cobalt.

LAMINATED MATERIALS

Plywood is an example of a laminated material. It is made by glueing together thin sheets of wood with their grain directions at right angles to each other (*Figure 8.8*). The grain directions are the directions of the cellulose fibres in the wood and thus the resulting structure, the plywood, has fibres in mutually perpendicular directions. Thus whereas the thin sheet had properties that were directional the resulting laminate has no such directionality.

The term *laminated wood* is generally used to describe the product obtained by sticking together thin sheets of wood but with the grain of each layer parallel to the grain of the others. Large wooden arches and beams in modern buildings are likely to be laminated rather than a solid piece of wood. By carefully choosing

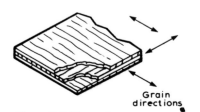

Figure 8.8 Plywood

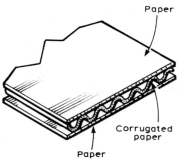

Paper

Corrugated
paper

Paper

Figure 8.9 Corugated cardboard

the wood used to build up the beam a better quality beam can be produced than would otherwise be produced by nature.

It is not only wood that is laminated, metals are too. The *cladding* of aluminium-copper alloy with aluminium to give a material with a better corrosion resistance than that of the alloy alone is an obvious example. Galvanised steel can be considered another example, a layer of zinc on the steel in order to give better corrosion resistance. Steel for use in food containers is often plated with tin to improve corrosion resistance. Many of the metals clad or plated with other metals are in this form for improved corrosion resistance.

Corrugated cardboard is another form of laminated structure (*Figure 8.9*), consisting of paper corrugations sandwiched between layers of paper. The resulting structure is much stiffer, in the direction parallel to the corrugations, than the paper alone. A similar type of material is produced with metals, a metal *honeycomb structure* sandwiched between thin sheets of metal. Such a structure has good stiffness and is very light. Aluminium is often used for both the honeycomb and the sheets.

PROBLEMS

1 Explain the term composite.

2 Give examples of composites involving (a) plastics and (b) metals.

3 Describe how the mechanical properties of a fibre composite depend on the form of the fibres and their orientation.

4 Calculate the tensile modulus of a composite consisting of 45% by volume of long glass fibres, tensile modulus 76 kN mm^{-2}, in a polyester matrix, tensile modulus 4 kN mm^{-2}. In what direction does your answer give the modulus?

5 In place of the glass fibres referred to in Question 4, carbon fibres are used. What would be the tensile modulus of the composite if the carbon fibres had a tensile modulus of 400 kN mm^{-2}?

6 What is a cermet?

7 Explain how plywood gets its stiffness.

8 Explain how corrugated cardboard gets its stiffness.

9 Long boron fibres, tensile modulus 340 kN mm^{-2}, are used to make a composite with aluminium as the matrix, tensile modulus 70 kN mm^{-2}. What would be the tensile modulus of the composite in the direction of the fibres if the fibres constitute 50 per cent of the volume of the composite?

10 Explain what is meant by the term 'dispersion strengthened metals' and give an example of one.

9 Fracture

Objectives   At the end of this chapter you should be able to:

- *Explain what is meant by allowable working stress and factor of safety.*
- *Distinguish between brittle and ductile fractures.*
- *Describe the factors affecting fracture.*

ALLOWABLE WORKING STRESS   Generally an important factor in the choice of material for a component is that the material should not fracture when the component is in use. Tensile or compressive tests can be used to determine the stress–strain graph for a material (see Chapter 2). Thus, it might be considered that a material in use should not be stressed beyond its yield or proof stress – the stress at which, if ductile, it would suffer plastic deformation or, if brittle, it would be close to fracture. However, the tensile test only puts the material under a uni-axial stress, i.e. stress in just one direction. In practice a component may well be subject to multi-axial stresses. For this reason and for reasons of safety, the maximum allowable working stress is calculated as a proportion of the yield or proof stress.

A factor of safety is used to arrive at the maximum allowable working stress. This factor is generally now expressed as

$$\text{Factor of safety} = \frac{\text{yield of stress}}{\text{maximum allowable stress}}$$

An alternative way of defining the safety factor is

$$\text{Factor of safety} = \frac{\text{tensile strength}}{\text{maximum allowable stress}}$$

Example
Using the yield stress definition of factor of safety, calculate the maximum allowable stress for a component made using a material having a yield stress of 200 N mm^{-2} if the factor of safety is 5.

$$\text{Maximum allowable stress} = \frac{\text{yield stress}}{\text{factor of safety}}$$

$$= \frac{200}{5} = 40 \text{ N mm}^{-2}$$

TYPES OF FRACTURE   When a ductile material has a gradually increasing stress applied it behaves elastically up to a limiting stress and then beyond that stress plastic deformation occurs. In the case of a tensile stress this deformation takes the form of necking (*Figure 9.1(a)*). As the stress is increased, the cross-sectional area of the material becomes considerably reduced until at some stress failure occurs. The fracture shows a typical cone and cup formation, which results because under the action of the increasing stress small internal cracks form which gradually grow in size until there is an internal,

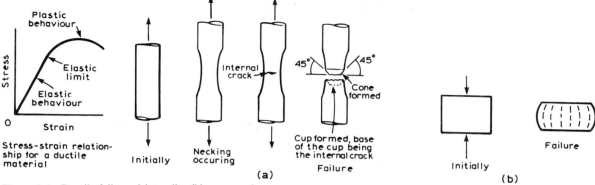

Figure 9.1 Ductile failure, (a) tensile, (b) compressive

almost horizontal crack. The final fracture occurs when the material shears at an angle of 45° to the axis of the direct stresses. This type of failure is known as a *ductile fracture*.

Materials can fail in a ductile manner in compression. Such failures show a characteristic bulge and a series of axial cracks around the edge of the material (*Figure 9.1(b)*).

Another form of failure is known as *brittle fracture*. If you drop a china cup and it breaks it is possible to pick up the pieces and stick them together again and have something which still looks like a cup. The china cup has failed by a brittle fracture. If you had dropped a tin mug then it might have deformed and show a dent. If you could have broken the tin mug it would not have been possible to stick the pieces together and have something that looked like the original tin mug. If somebody drives a car into a wall the metal car wings are most likely to show a ductile failure like the tin mug. With a brittle failure the material fractures before any significant plastic deformation has occurred.

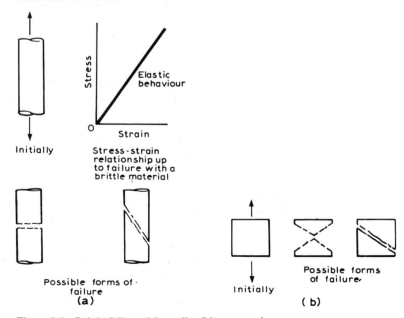

Figure 9.2 Brittle failure, (a) tensile, (b) compressive

Figure 9.2(a) shows the possible forms of a brittle tensile fracture. The surface of the fractured material appears bright and granular due to the reflection of light from individual crystal surfaces. *Figure 9.2(b)* shows the possible forms of a brittle compressive failure.

FACTORS AFFECTING FRACTURE

If you want to break a piece of material, one way you can adopt is to make a small notch in the surface of the material and then apply a force. The presence of a notch or any sudden change in section of a piece of material can very significantly change the stress at which fracture occurs. The notch or sudden change in section produces what are called *stress concentrations*. They disturb the assumed stress distribution and produce local concentrations of stress.

The amount by which the stress is raised depends on the depth of the notch, or change in section, and the radius of the tip of the notch. The greater the depth of the notch and/or the smaller the radius of the tip of the notch, the greater the amount by which the stress is raised.

A crack in a brittle material will have a quite pointed tip and hence a small radius. Such a crack thus produces a large increase in stress at its tip. One way of arresting the progress of such a crack is to drill a hole at the end of the crack to increase its radius and so reduce the stress concentration.

An approximate relationship that has been derived for the stress at the end of a notch is

Stress at end of notch = applied stress $\times [1 + 2\sqrt{(L/r)}]$

where L is the length of the notch and r the radius, of the tip of the notch. The increase in stress due to the notch is thus

Increase in stress = $2\sqrt{(L/r)}$

A crack in a ductile material is less likely to lead to failure than in a brittle material because a high stress concentration at the end of a notch leads to plastic flow and so an increase in the radius of the tip of the notch. The result is a decrease in the stress concentration.

Another factor which can affect the behaviour of a material is the speed of loading. A sharp blow to the material may lead to a fracture where the same stress applied more slowly would not. With a very high rate of application of stress there may be insufficient time for plastic deformation of the material to occur and so what was under normal conditions a ductile material behaves as though it were brittle. If a material has a notch or change in section and is subject to a sudden impact, the dual effects of the stress concentration due to the notch and the material behaving as though brittle can result in failure.

The Charpy and Izod tests referred to in Chapter 2 give a measure of the behaviour of a notched sample of material when subject to a sudden impact load. The results are expressed in terms of the energy needed to break a standard size test specimen; the smaller the energy needed to break the specimen, the easier it will be for failure to occur in service. The smaller energies are associated with materials which are termed brittle; ductile materials need higher energies for fracture to occur.

The temperature of a material when it is subject to stress can affect its behaviour, many metals which are ductile at high tempera-

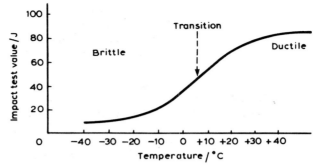

Figure 9.3 Ductile/brittle transition

tures being brittle at low temperatures. *Figure 9.3* shows how the impact test results for a steel change with temperature. At room temperature and above the steel behaves as a ductile material; below 0°C it behaves as a brittle material. The *transition* temperature at which the change from ductile to brittle behaviour occurs is thus of importance in determining how a material will behave in service.

The transition temperature with a steel is affected by the alloying elements in the steel. Manganese and nickel reduce the transition temperature. Thus for low-temperature work a steel with these alloying elements should be preferred. Carbon, nitrogen and phosphorous increase the transition temperature.

PROBLEMS

1 Explain the term *safety factor*.

2 Calculate the maximum allowable stress for a component made with a material having a yield stress of $110\,N\,mm^{-2}$ if the factor of safety is 5.

3 Distinguish between ductile and brittle fractures.

4 Given a fractured specimen, what would you look for in order to determine whether the fracture was a ductile or a brittle fracture?

5 How does the presence of a notch or an abrupt change in section affect failure behaviour?

6 Does a plastic spoon exhibit brittle or ductile fracture when broken at room temperature? Does the type of fracture depend on the temperature of the spoon? (Try an investigation.)

10 Fatigue

Objectives   At the end of this chapter you should be able to:

- *Explain what is meant by fatigue failure.*
- *Describe the types of fatigue tests used, explaining the terms stress, amplitude, fatigue limit, endurance limit and S/N graphs.*
- *Describe the main factors affecting the fatigue properties of metals.*
- *Describe the fatigue properties of plastics.*
- *Interpret fatigue data.*

FATIGUE FAILURE

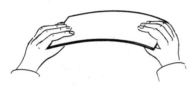

Figure 10.1

If you take a stiff piece of metal or plastic, and want to break it, then you will most likely flex the strip back and forth, as in *Figure 10.1*. This is generally an easier way of causing the material to fail than applying a direct pull.

In service many components undergo thousands, often millions, of changes of stress. Some are repeatedly stressed and unstressed, while some undergo alternating stresses of compression and tension. For others the stress may just fluctuate about some value. Many materials subject to such conditions fail, even though the maximum stress in any one stress change is less than the fracture stress as determined by a simple tensile test. Such a failure, as a result of repeated stressing, is called a *fatigue failure* (*Figure 10.2*).

The source of the alternating stresses can be due to the conditions of use of a component. Thus, in the case of an aircraft, the changes

Figure 10.2 Fatigue failure of a large shaft. (From John, V.B., *Introduction to Engineering Materials*, by permission of Macmillan, London and Basingstoke)

of pressure between the cabin and the outside of the aircraft every time it flies subject the cabin skin to repeated stressing. Components such as a crown wheel and pinion are subject to repeated stressing by the very way in which they are used, while others receive their stressing 'accidentally'. Vibration of the component can occur as a result of the transmission of vibration from some machine nearby. Turbine blades may vibrate in use in such a way that they fail by fatigue. It has been said that fatigue causes at least 80 per cent of the failures in modern engineering components.

A fatigue crack often starts at some point of stress concentration. This point of origin of the failure can be seen on the failed material as a smooth, flat, semicircular or elliptical region, often referred to as the nucleus. Surrounding the nucleus is a burnished zone with ribbed markings. This smooth zone is produced by the crack propagating relatively slowly through the material and the resulting fractured surfaces rubbing together during the alternating stressing of the component. When the component has become so weakened by the crack that it is no longer able to carry the load, the final, abrupt fracture occurs, which shows a typically crystalline appearance. *Figure 10.3* shows the various stages in the growth of a fatigue crack failure.

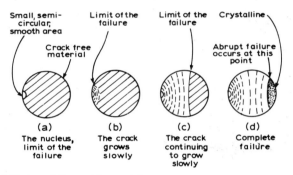

Figure 10.3 Fatigue failure with a metal

FATIGUE TESTS

Fatigue tests can be carried out in a number of ways, the way used being the one needed to simulate the type of stress changes that will occur to the material of a component when in service. There are thus bending-stress machines which bend a test piece of the material alternately one way and then the other (*Figure 10.4(a)*), and torsional-fatigue machines which twist the test piece alternately one way and then the other (*Figure 10.4(b)*). Another type of machine can be used to produce alternating tension and compression by direct stressing (*Figure 10.4(c)*).

The tests can be carried out with stresses which alternate about zero stress (*Figure 10.4(d)*), apply a repeated stress which varies from zero to some maximum stress (*Figure 10.4(e)*) or apply a stress which varies about some stress value and does not reach zero at all (*Figure 10.4(f)*).

In the case of the alternating stress (*Figure 10.4(d)*), the stress varies between $+S$ and $-S$. The tensile stress is denoted by a positive sign, the compressive stress by a negative sign; the stress range is thus $2S$. The mean stress is zero as the stress alternates

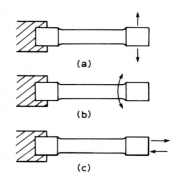

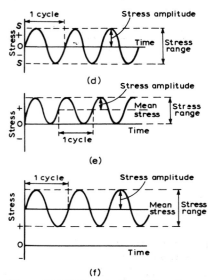

Figure 10.4 Fatigue testing (a) bending (b) torsion (c) direct stress (d) alternating stress (e) repeated stress (f) fluctuating stress

equally about the zero stress. With the repeated stress (*Figure 10.4(e)*), the mean stress is half the stress range. With the fluctuating stress (*Figure 10.4(f)*) the mean stress is more than half the stress range.

In the fatigue tests, the machine is kept running, alternating the stress, until the specimen fails, the number of cycles of stressing up to failure being recorded by the machine. The test is repeated for the specimen subject to different stress ranges. Such tests enable graphs similar to those in *Figure 10.5* to be plotted. The vertical axis is the *stress amplitude*, half the stress range. For a stress amplitude greater than the value given by the graph line, failure occurs for the number of cycles concerned. These graphs are known as *S/N graphs*, the *S* denoting the stress amplitude and the *N* the number of cycles.

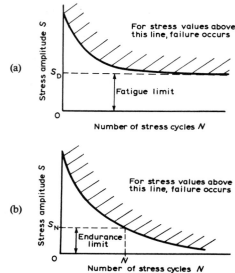

Figure 10.5 Typical *S/N* graphs for (a) a steel (b) a non-ferrous alloy

For the *S/N* graph in *Figure 10.5(a)* there is a stress amplitude for which the material will endure an indefinite number of stress cycles. The maximum value, S_D, being called the *fatigue limit*. For any stress amplitude greater than the fatigue limit, failure will occur if the material undergoes a sufficient number of stress cycles. With the *S/N* graph shown in *Figure 10.5(b)* there is no stress amplitude at which failure cannot occur; for such materials as *endurance limit* S_N is quoted. This is defined as the maximum stress amplitude which can be sustained for *N* cycles.

The number of reversals that a specimen can sustain before failure occurs depends on the stress amplitude, the bigger the stress amplitude the smaller the number of cycles of stress and reversals that can be sustained.

Some typical results for an aluminium alloy specimen are:

Stress amplitude/MN m^{-2}	Number of cycles before failure/$\times 10^6$
185	1
155	5
145	10
120	50
115	100

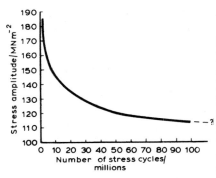

Figure 10.6 *S/N* graph for an aluminium alloy

With a stress amplitude of 185 MN m^{-2}, e.g. a stress alternating from +185 MN m^{-2} to −185 MN m^{-2}, one million cycles are needed before failure occurs. With a smaller stress amplitude of 115 MN m^{-2} one hundred million cycles are needed before failure occurs. *Figure 10.6* shows the *S/N* graph for the above data. Extrapolation of the graph seems to indicate that for a greater number of cycles, failure will occur at even smaller stress amplitudes. There seems to be no stress amplitude for which failure will not occur; the material has no fatigue limit. If a component made of that material had a service life of 100 million stress cycles then we could specify that during the life-time, failure should not occur for stress amplitudes less than 115 MN m^{-2}. The endurance limit for 100 million cycles is thus 115 MN m$^-$.

The following are some typical results for a steel, the fatigue tests being bending stress (*Figure 10.7*):

Stress amplitude/MN m^{-2}	Number of cycles before failure ($\times 10^6$)
750	0.01
550	0.1
450	1
450	10
450	100

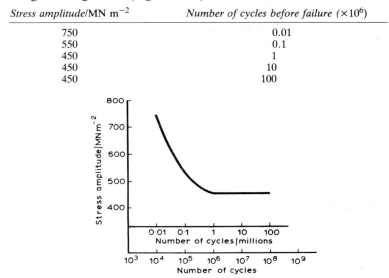

Figure 10.7 *S/N* graph for a steel. Note: number of cycles shown on logarithmic scale

With a stress amplitude of 750 MN m^{-2}, e.g. a stress alternating from +750 NM m^{-2} to −750 MN m^{-2}, 0.01 million cycles or ten thousand cycles are needed before failure occurs. For one million, ten million and one hundred million cycles the stress amplitude for failure is the same, 450 MN m^{-2}. For stress amplitudes below this value the material should not fail, however long the test continues. The fatigue limit is thus 450 MN m^{-2}.

The fatigue limit, or the endurance limit at about 500 million cycles, for metals tends to lie between about a third and a half of the static tensile strength. This applies to most steels, aluminium alloys, brass, nickel and magnesium alloys. For example, a steel with a tensile strength of 420 MN m^{-2} has a fatigue limit of 180 MN m^{-2}, just under half the tensile strength. If used in a situation where it were subject to alternating stresses, such a steel would need to be limited to stress amplitudes below 180 MN m^{-2} if it were not to fail at some time. A magnesium alloy with a tensile strength of 290 MN m^{-2} has an endurance limit of 120 MN m^{-2}, just under half the tensile strength. Such an alloy would need to be limited to stress amplitudes below 120 MN m^{-2} if it were to last to 500 million cycles.

Table 10.1   Typical manufacturers' information concerning grey cast irons (Courtesy of BCIRA)

Fatigue limit
For grey cast irons with tensile strengths of 150–300 N mm^{-2} the fatigue limit is about 45 per cent of the tensile strength. At higher stresses the ratio decreases, and values of 0.425 and 0.38 have been considered typical of irons with tensile strengths of 350 and 400 N mm^{-2}.

Grey cast irons are relatively insensitive to notches in fatigue; normally a notch will not reduce the fatigue limit in an iron with a tensile strength of 150 N mm^{-2}. In an iron with a tensile strength of 400 N mm^{-2} notching has been found to reduce the fatigue limit to about 83 per cent of the unnotched value.

FACTORS AFFECTING THE FATIGUE PROPERTIES OF METALS

The main factors affecting the fatigue properties of a component are:

1 Stress concentrations caused by component design.
2 Corrosion.
3 Residual stresses.
4 Surface finish.
5 Temperature.

Fatigue of a component depends on the stress amplitude attained, the bigger the stress amplitude the fewer the stress cycles needed for failure. Stress concentrations caused by sudden changes in cross-section, keyways, holes or sharp corners can thus more easily lead to a fatigue failure. The presence of a countersunk hole was considered in one case to have lead to a stress concentration which could have led to a fatigue failure. *Figure 10.8* shows the effect on the fatigue properties of a steel of a small hole acting as a stress raiser. With the hole, at every stress amplitude value less cycles are needed to reach failure. There is also a lower fatigue limit with the hole present, 700 MN m^{-2} instead of over 1000 MN m^{-2}.

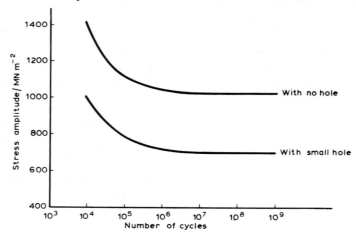

Figure 10.8 *S/N* graph for a steel both with and without small hole acting as stress raiser. Note: number of cycles shown on logarithmic scale

Figure 10.9 shows the effect on the fatigue properties of a steel of exposure to salt solution. The effect of the corrosion resulting from the salt solution attack on the steel is to reduce the number of stress cycles needed to reach failure for every stress amplitude. The non-corroded steel has a fatigue limit of 450 MN^{-2}, the corroded steel has no fatigue limit. There is thus no stress amplitude below which failure will not occur. The steel can be protected against the corrosion by plating; for example, chromium or zinc plating of the steel can result in the same *S/N* graph as the non-corroded steel even though it is subject to a corrosive atmosphere (see Chapter 12 for a further discussion of corrosion).

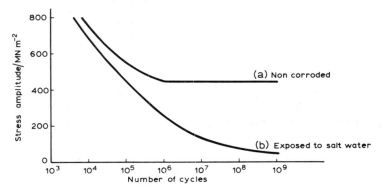

Figure 10.9 *S/N* graph for a steel, (a) with no corrosion and (b) corroded by exposure to salt solution. Note: number of cycles shown on logarithmic scale

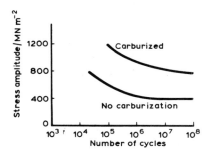

Figure 10.10 *S/N* graph for a steel, showing effect of carburisation. Note: number of cycles shown on logarithmic scale

Residual stresses can be produced by many fabrication and finishing processes. If the stresses produced are such that the surfaces have compressive residual stresses then the fatigue properties are improved, but if tensile residual stresses are produced at the surfaces then poorer fatigue properties result. The case-hardening of steels by carburising results in compressive residual stresses at the surface, hence carburising improves the fatigue properties. *Figure 10.10* shows the effect of carburising a hardened steel. Many machining processes result in the production of surface tensile residual stresses and so result in poorer fatigue properties.

The effect of surface finish on the fatigue properties of a component is very significant. Scratches, dents or even surface identification markings can act as stress raisers and so reduce the fatigue properties. Shot peening a surface produces surface compressive residual stresses and improves the fatigue performance.

An increase in temperature can lead to a reduction in fatigue properties as a consequence of oxidation or corrosion of the metal surface increasing. For example, the nickel-chromium alloy Nimonic 90 undergoes surface degradation at temperatures around 700 to 800°C and there is a poorer fatigue performance as a result. In many instances an increase in temperature does result in a poorer fatigue performance.

THE FATIGUE PROPERTIES OF PLASTICS

Fatigue tests can be carried out on plastics in the same way as with metals. A factor not present with metals is that when a plastic is subject to an alternating stress it becomes significantly warmer. The faster the stress is alternated, i.e., the higher the frequency of the alternating stress, the greater the temperature rise. Under very high frequency alternating stresses the temperature rise may be large enough to melt the plastic. To avoid this, fatigue tests are normally carried out with lower-frequency alternating stresses than is usual with metals. The results of such tests, however, are not entirely valid if the alternating stresses experienced by the plastic component in service are higher than those used for the test.

Figure 10.11 shows an *S/N* graph for a plastic, unplasticised PVC. The alternating stresses were applied with a square waveform at a frequency of 0.5 Hz, i.e. a change of stress every 2 s. The graph seems to indicate that there will be no stress amplitude for which failure will not occur; the material thus seems to have no fatigue limit.

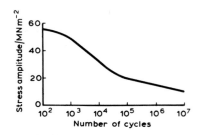

Figure 10.11   *S/N* graph for unplasticised PVC, alternating stress being a square waveform at frequency 0.5 Hz. Note: number of cycles shown on logarithmic scale

PROBLEMS

1 Explain what is meant by fatigue failure.

2 List the types of test available for the determination of the fatigue properties of specimens.

3 Describe the various stages in the failure of a component by fatigue.

4 Explain the terms 'fatigue limit' and 'endurance limit'.

5 *Figure 10.6* shows the *S/N* graph for an aluminium alloy.

(a) For how many stress cycles could a stress amplitude of 140 MN m^{-2} be sustained before failure occurs?

(b) What would be the maximum stress amplitude that should be applied if the component made of the material is to last for 50 million stress cycles?

(c) The alloy has a tensile strength of 400 MN m^{-2} and a yield stress of 280 MN m^{-2}. What should be the limiting stress when such an alloy is used for static conditions? What should be the limiting stress when the alloy is used for dynamic conditions where the number of cycles is not likely to exceed 10 million?

6 Explain an *S/N* graph and state the information that can be extracted from the graph.

7 What is the fatigue limit for the uncarburised steel giving the *S/N* graph in *Figure 10.10*?

8 What is the endurance limit for the unplasticized PVC at 10^6 cycles that gave the *S/N* graph in *Figure 10.11*?

9 Plot the *S/N* graph for the nickel-chromium alloy Nimonic 90, which gave the following fatigue test results. Determine from the graph the fatigue limit.

Stress amplitude/MN m^{-2}	Number of cycles before failure
750	10^5
480	10^6
350	10^7
320	10^8
320	10^9
320	10^{10}

10 Plot the *S/N* graph for the plastic (cast acrylic) which gave the following fatigue test results when tested with a square waveform at 0.5 Hz. Why specify this frequency? What is the endurance limit at 10^6 cycles?

Stress amplitude/MN m^{-2}	Number of cycles before failure
70	10^2
62	10^3
58	10^4
55	10^5
41	10^6
31	10^7

11 *Figure 10.12* shows the *S/N* graph for a nickel-based alloy Iconel 718.

(a) What is the fatigue limit?

(b) What is the significance of the constant stress amplitude part of the graph from 10^0 to 10^4 cycles?

(c) The graph is for the material at 600°C. The tensile strength at that temperature is 100 MN m^{-2}. What can be added to your answer to part (b)?

12 *Figure 10.13* shows two *S/N* graphs, one for the material in an un-notched state, the other for the material with a notch. Which of the graphs would you expect to represent each condition? Give reasons for your answer.

13 List factors that contribute to the onset of fatigue failure and those which tend to resist fatigue.

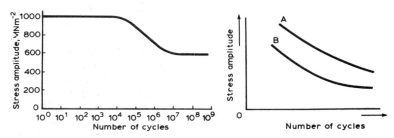

Figure 10.12 *S/N* graph for a nickel-based alloy, Iconel 718

Figure 10.13

11 Creep

Objectives At the end of this chapter you should be able to:

● *Describe the essential features of a creep test and the type of results produced.*
● *Explain the terms primary creep, secondary creep, tertiary creep, stress to rupture, isochronous stress/strain graph, creep modulus.*
● *Describe the main factors affecting the creep properties of metals and plastics.*
● *Interpret creep data.*

SHORT-TERM AND LONG-TERM BEHAVIOR

There are many situations where a piece of material is exposed to a stress for a protracted period of time. The stress/strain data obtained from the conventional tensile test refer generally to a situation where the stresses are applied for quite short intervals of time and so the strain results refer only to the immediate values resulting from stresses. Suppose stress were applied to a piece of material and the stress remained acting on the material for a long time – what would be the result? If you tried such an experiment with a strip of lead you would find that the strain would increase with time – the material would increase in length with time even though the stress remained constant. This phenomenon is called *creep*, which can be defined as the continuing deformation of a material with the passage of time when the material is subject to a constant stress.

For metals, other than the very soft metals like lead, creep effects are negligible at ordinary temperatures, but however become significant at high temperatures. For plastics, creep is often quite significant at ordinary temperatures and even more noticeable at higher temperatures.

Figure 11.1 shows the essential features of a creep test. A constant stress is applied to the specimen, sometimes by the simple method of suspending loads from it. Because creep tests with metals are usually performed at high temperatures a furnace surrounds the specimen, the temperature of the furnace being held constant by a thermostat. The temperature of the specimen is generally measured by a thermocouple attached to it.

Figure 11.2 shows the general form of results from a creep test. The curve generally has three parts. During the *primary creep* period the strain is changing but the rate at which it is changing with time decreases. During the *secondary creep* period the strain increases steadily with time at a constant rate. During the *tertiary creep* period the rate at which the strain is changing increases and eventually causes failure. Thus the initial stress, which did not produce early failure, will result in a failure after some period of time. Such an initial stress is referred to as the *stress to rupture* in some particular time. Thus an acrylic plastic may have a rupture stress of 50 N mm⁻² at room temperature for failure in one week.

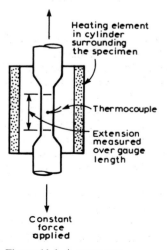

Heating element in cylinder surrounding the specimen

Thermocouple

Extension measured over gauge length

Constant force applied

Figure 11.1 A creep test

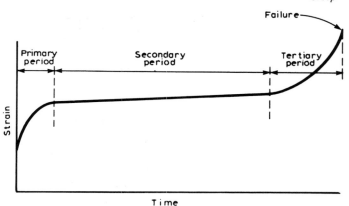

Figure 11.2 Typical creep curve for a metal

FACTORS AFFECTING CREEP BEHAVIOUR WITH METALS

For a particular material, the creep behaviour depends on both the temperature and the initial stress; the higher the temperature the greater the creep, also the higher the stress the greater the creep. *Figure 11.3* shows both these effects. Thus to minimise creep, the conditions need to be low stress and low temperature.

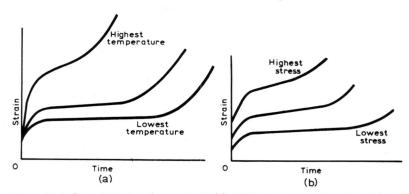

Figure 11.3 Creep behaviour for a material (a) at different temperatures but subject to constant stress (b) at different stresses but subject to constant temperature

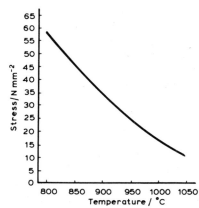

Figure 11.4 Data to give 1% creep in 10 000 h for Pireks 25/20 alloy (0.45% C, 0.8% Mn, 1.2% Si, 20% Cr, 25% Ni). (Courtesy of Darwins Alloy Castings Ltd)

Figure 11.4 shows one way of presenting creep data, indicating the design stress that can be permitted at any temperature if the creep is to be kept within specified limits. In the example given, the limit is 1% creep in 10 000 hours. Thus for the Pireks 25/20 nickel-chrome alloy a stress of 58.6 N mm^{-2} at a temperature of 800°C will produce the 1% creep in 10 000 h. At 1050°C a stress of only 10.3 N mm^{-2} will produce the same creep in 10 000 h. *Figure 11.5* shows how stress to rupture the material in 10 000 h varies with temperature. At 800°C a stress of 65.0 N mm^{-2} will result in the Pireks 25/20 alloy failing in 10 000 h; at 1050°C a stress of only 14.5 N mm^{-2} will result in failure in the same time.

Another factor that determines the creep behaviour of a metal is its composition. *Figure 11.6* shows how the stress to rupture different materials in 1000 h varies with temperature. Aluminium alloys fail at quite low stresses when the temperature rises over 200°C. Titanium alloys can be used at higher temperatures before the stress

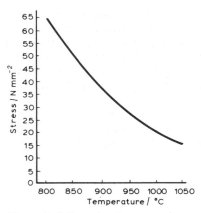

Figure 11.5 Data showing stress to rupture at 10 000 h for Pireks 25/20 alloy. (See also *Figure 4.4*)

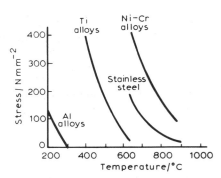

Figure 11.6 Stress to rupture in 1000 h for different materials

to rupture drops to very low values, while stainless steel is even better and nickel-chromium alloys offer yet better resistance to creep.

FACTORS AFFECTING CREEP BEHAVIOUR WITH PLASTICS

While creep is significant mainly for metals at high temperatures, creep can be significant with plastics at normal temperatures. The creep behaviour of a plastic depends on temperature and stress, just like metals. It also depends on the type of plastic involved – flexible plastics show more creep than stiff ones.

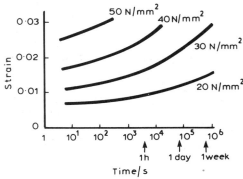

Figure 11.7 Creep behaviour of polyacetal at different stresses. Note logarithmic timescale

Figure 11.7 shows how the strain on a sample of polyacetal at 20°C varies with time for different stresses. The higher the stress the greater the creep. As can be seen from the graph, the plastic creeps quite substantially in a period of just over a week, even at relatively low stresses.

Figure 11.7 is the form of graph obtained by plotting of results derived from creep tests. Based on the *Figure 11.7* graph of strain against time at different stresses a graph of stress against strain for different times can be produced. Thus for a time of 10^2 s, a vertical line drawn on *Figure 11.7* enables the stresses needed for different strains after this time to be read from the graph (*Figure 11.8 (a)*). The resulting stress/strain graph is shown in *Figure 11.8(b)* and is known as an *isochronous stress/strain graph*. For a specific time the

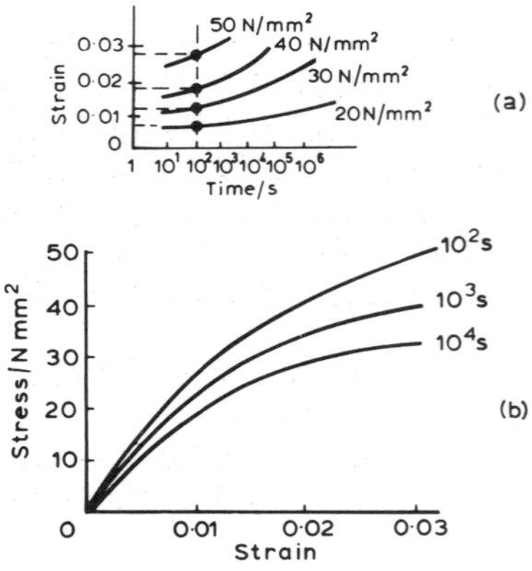

Figure 11.8 (a) Obtaining stress/strain data (b) isochronous stress/strain graph

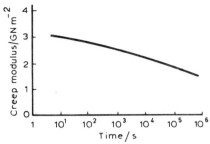

Figure 11.9 Variation of creep modulus with time for polyacetal at 0.5% strain and 20°C

quantity obtained by dividing the stress by the strain for the isochronous stress/strain graph can be calculated and is known as the *creep modulus*. It is not the same as Young's modulus though it can be used to compare the stiffness of plastics. The creep modulus varies both with time and strain and *Figure 11.9* shows how, at 0.5% strain and 20°C it varies with time for the polyacetal described in *Figure 11.7* and *11.8*.

Figure 11.10 shows how the stress to rupture a plastic, Durethan – polyamide, varies with time at different temperatures. The higher the temperature the lower the stress needed to rupture the material after any particular time.

PROBLEMS

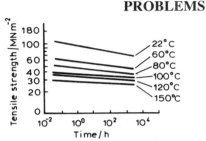

Figure 11.10 Creep rupture graph for Durethan BKV 30 (Courtesy Bayer UK Ltd)

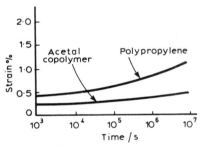

Figure 11.11

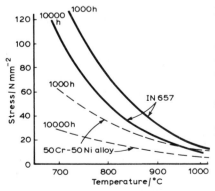

Figure 11.12 Creep rupture data from 'High chromium Cr-Ni alloys to resist residual fuel oils ash corrosion'. (Courtesy of Inco Europe Ltd)

1 Explain what is meant by 'creep'.

2 Describe the form of a typical strain/time graph resulting from a creep test and explain the significance of the slope of the graph at its various stages.

3 Describe the effect of (a) increased stress and (b) increased temperature on the creep behaviour of materials.

4 For the alloy described in *Figure 11.4*, estimate the stress that will result in a 1% creep at a temperature of 900°C after 10 000 h.

5 For the alloy described in *Figure 11.5*, estimate the stress to rupture at 10 000 h for a temperature of 900°C.

6 Under what circumstances, would you consider that a metal like that described in *Figure 11.4* and *11.5*, would be necessary? What would you estimate the limiting temperature for use of such an alloy?

7 Explain how an isochronous stress/strain graph for a polymer can be obtained from creep test results.

8 Explain the significance of the graph shown in *Figure 11.10* for the creep rupture behaviours of Durethan.

9 Durethan, as described by *Figure 11.10*, is used for car fan blades, fuse box covers, door handles and plastic seats. How would the behaviour of the material change when the temperature or stress rises?

10 *Figure 11.11* shows how the strain changes with time for two different polymers when they are subjected to a constant stress. Describe how the materials will creep with time. Which material will creep the most?

11 *Figure 11.12* shows the stress rupture properties of two alloys, one 50% chromium and 50% nickel, the other (IN 657) 48–52% chromium, 1.4–1.7% niobium, 0.1% carbon, 0.16% nitrogen, 0.2% carbon + nitrogen, 0.5% maximum silicon, 1.0% iron, 0.3% maximum manganese and the remainder nickel. The creep rupture data is presented for two different times, 1000 h and 10 000 h.

(a) What is the significance of the difference between the 1000 h and 10 000 h graphs?

(b) What is the difference in behaviour of the 50 Cr–50 Ni alloy and the IN 657 alloy when temperatures increase?

(c) The IN 657 alloy is said to show 'improved hot strength' when compared with the 50 Cr–50 Ni alloy. Explain this statement.

12 Environmental stability of materials

Objectives At the end of this chapter you should be able to:

- *Describe the process of corrosion, explaining such terms as galvanic corrosion, galvanic series, demetallification, graphitisation, concentration cell, stress corrosion, differential aeration cells.*
- *Describe methods of corrosion prevention involving selection of materials, selection of design, modification of the environment and protective coatings.*
- *Describe the factors affecting the stability of polymers and ceramics.*
- *Identify potential corrosion situations.*

CORROSION The car owner can rightly be concerned about rust patches appearing on the bodywork of the car, as the rust not only makes the bodywork look shoddy but indicates a mechanical weakening of the material. The steel used for the car bodywork has thus changed with time due to an interaction between it and the environment. The possibility of such corrosion is therefore a factor that has to be taken into account when a material is selected for a particular purpose.

Most metals react, at moderate temperatures, only slowly with the oxygen in the air. The result is the build up of a layer of oxide on the surface of the metal, which can insulate the metal from further reaction with the oxygen. Aluminium is an example of a metal that builds up a protective oxide layer which is a very effective barrier against further oxidation. If oxidation were the only reaction which tended to occur between a metal and its environment then probably corrosion would present few problems. The presence of moisture in the environment can very markedly affect corrosion, as can the presence of chemically active pollutants.

Iron rusts when the environment contains both oxygen and moisture, but not with oxygen alone or moisture alone. Iron nails kept in a container with dry air do not rust, nor if they are kept in oxygen-free, e.g. boiled, water. But in moist air they rust readily.

Chemically-active pollutants in the environment can have a marked effect on corrosion, especially those that are soluble in water. Man-made pollutants such as the oxides of carbon and sulphur, produced in the combustion of fuels, dissolve in water to give acids, which readily attack metals and many other materials. Marine environments also are particularly corrosive, due to the high concentrations of salt from the sea. The sodium chloride reacts with metals to produce chlorides of the metals which are soluble in water and thus cannot act as a protective layer on the surface of a metal as a non-soluble oxide may do. The salt may also destroy the protective oxide layer that has been acquired by a metal.

GALVANIC CORROSION A simple electrical cell could be just a plate of copper and one of zinc (*Figure 12.1*) dipping into an *electrolyte*, a solution that conducts

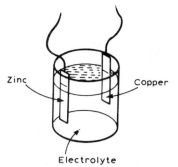

Figure 12.1 A simple cell

electricity. Such a cell gives a potential difference between the two metals – it can be measured with a voltmeter or used to light a lamp. Different pairs of metals give different potential differences. Thus a zinc-copper cell gives a potential difference of about 1.1 V, and an iron-copper cell about 0.8 V. A zinc-iron cell gives a potential difference of about 0.3 V; this value is however the difference between the potential differences of the zinc-copper and iron-copper cells. It is as though we had a cell made up with zinc-copper-iron.

By tabulating values of the potential differences between the various metals and standard, a table can be produced from which the potential differences between any pair of metals can be forecast. The standard used is hydrogen and the following are the potential differences relative to hydrogen for a number of metals.

Metal	Potential difference/V
Gold	+1.7
Silver	+0.80
Copper	+0.34
Hydrogen	0.00
Lead	−0.13
Tin	−0.14
Nickel	−0.25
Iron	−0.44
Zinc	−0.76
Aluminium	−1.67
Magnesium	−2.34
Sodium	−2.71

The table gives, for a silver-aluminium cell, a potential difference of 2.47 V, that is +0.80 − (−1.67) V. The metal highest up the table, as shown above, behaves as the negative electrode of the cell while the metal lowest in the table is the positive electrode. The term *cathode* is used for the negative electrode and *anode* for the positive electrode. Thus for the silver-aluminium cell the silver is the negative electrode and the aluminium the positive electrode.

With a copper-zinc cell it is found that the copper electrode remains unchanged after a period of cell use but the zinc electrode is badly corroded. With any cell the anode is corroded and the cathode not affected. The greater the cell potential difference the greater the corrosion of the anode.

The above table lists what is called the *electromotive series* or *galvanic series*. Tables of such series are available for metals in various environments. Such tables are of use in assessing the possibilities of corrosion when two different metals are in electrical contact, either directly or through a common electrolyte.

If a copper pipe is connected to a galvanised steel tank, perhaps the cold water storage tank in your home, a cell is created (*Figure 12.2*) and corrosion follows. Galvanised steel is zinc-coated steel; there is thus a copper-zinc cell. With such a cell the copper is the cathode and the zinc the anode; the zinc thus corrodes and so exposes the iron. Iron-copper is also a good cell with the iron as the anode. The result is corrosion of the iron and hence the overall result of connecting the copper pipe to the tank is likely to be a leaking tank.

Stainless steel and mild steel form a cell, the mild steel being the anode. Thus if a stainless steel trim, on say a car, is in electrical

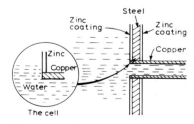

Figure 12.2 Copper-zinc cell for copper pipe connection to galvanised steel water tank

contact with mild steel bodywork, then the bodywork will corrode more rapidly than if no stainless steel trim were used. The electrical connection between the stainless steel and the mild steel may be through water gathering at the junction between the two. With oxygen-free clean water the cell potential difference may be only 0.15 V, but if the water were sea water containing oxygen the potential difference could become as high as 0.75 V. So the use of salt in Britain, to melt ice on the road, leads to greater corrosion of cars.

It is not only with two separate metals that cells can be produced and corrosion occur, as galvanic cells can be produced in a number of ways. An alloy or a metal containing impurities can give rise to galvanic cells within itself. For example, brass is an alloy of copper and zinc, a copper-zinc cell has the zinc as the anode and thus the zinc corrodes. The effect is called *dezincification*, one example of *demetallification*. After such corrosion the remaining metal is likely to be porous and lacking in mechanical strength.

A similar type of corrosion takes place for carbon steels in the pearlitic condition, the cementite in the steel acting as the cathode and the ferrite as the anode. The ferrite is thus corroded.

Cast-iron is a mixture of iron and graphite, the graphite acting as the cathode and the iron as the anode. The iron is thus corroded, the effect being known as *graphitisation*.

Variations in concentration of the electrolyte in contact with a metal can lead to corrosion. That part of the metal in contact with the more concentrated electrolyte acts as a cathode while the part in contact with the more dilute electrolyte acts as an anode and so corrodes most. Such a cell is known as a *concentration cell*.

Another type of concentration cell is produced if there are variations in the amount of oxygen dissolved in the water in contact with a metal. That part of the metal in contact with the water having the greatest concentration of oxygen acts as a cathode while the part of the metal in contact with the water having the least concentration acts as an anode and so corrodes most. A drop of water on a steel surface is likely to have a higher concentration of dissolved oxygen near its surface where it is in contact with air than in the centre of the drop (*Figure 12.3*). The metal at the centre of the drop acts as an anode and so corrodes most.

Variations in stress within a metal or a component can lead to the production of cells and hence corrosion. A component which has part of it heavily cold-worked and part less-worked will contain internal stresses which can result in the heavily-worked part acting as an anode and the less-worked part as a cathode. Therefore the heavily cold-worked part corrodes most.

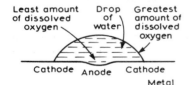

Figure 12.3 Example of a concentration cell

CORROSION PREVENTION

Methods of preventing corrosion, or reducing it, can be summarised as:

1 Selection of appropriate materials.
2 Selection of appropriate design.
3 Modification of the environment.
4 Use of protective coatings.

In selecting materials, care should be taken not to use two different materials in close proximity, particularly if they are far apart in the galvanic series, giving a high potential difference between them. The material which acts as the anode will be corroded in the appropriate environment. It is not desirable to connect copper pipes to steel water tanks. Steel pipes to a steel tank would be better.

However there are situations where the introduction of a dissimilar metal can be used for protection of another metal. Pieces of magnesium or zinc placed close to buried iron pipes can protect the pipes in that the magnesium or zinc acts as the anode relative to the iron which becomes the cathode. The result is corrosion of the magnesium or zinc and not the pipe. Such a method is known as *galvanic protection*.

The steel hull of a ship can be protected below the water line by fixing pieces of magnesium or zinc to it. The steel then behaves as the cathode, the magnesium or zinc becoming the anode and so corroding. Another way of making a piece of metal act as a cathode and so not corrode, is to connect it to a source of e.m.f. in such a way that the externally applied potential difference makes the metal the cathode in an electrical circuit (*Figure 12.4*).

Selection of an appropriate metal for a specific environment can do much to reduce corrosion. These are the properties of some metals in different environments.

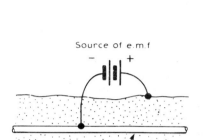

Figure 12.4 Corrosion prevention using an applied e.m.f.

Copper
When exposed to the atmosphere copper develops an adherent protective layer which then insulates it from further corrosion. Copper is used for water pipes, e.g. domestic water supply pipes, as it offers a high resistance to corrosion in such situations.

Copper alloys
Demetallification can occur. Some of the alloying metals, however, can improve the corrosion resistance of the copper by improving the development of the adherent protective surface layer.

Iron and steel
This is corroded readily in many environments and exposure to sea water can result in graphitisation. Stress corrosion can occur in certain environments.

Alloy steels
The addition of chromium to steel can improve considerably the corrosion resistance by modifying the surface protective film produced under oxidising conditions. The addition of nickel to an iron-chromium alloy can further improve corrosion resistance and such a material can be used in sea water with little corrosion resulting. Austenitic steels, however, are susceptible to stress corrosion in certain environments. Iron-nickel alloys have good corrosion resistance and such alloys with 20% nickel and 2 to 3% carbon are particularly good for marine environments.

Zinc
Zinc can develop a durable oxide layer in the atmosphere and then becomes resistant to corrosion.

Aluminium
Readily developing a durable protective surface film, aluminium is

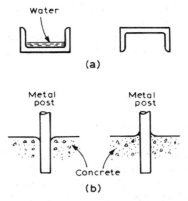

Figure 12.5 Ways of reducing corrosion by preventing water from collecting, (a) simple inversion (b) using a fillet to eliminate crevice

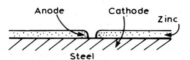

Figure 12.6 Galvanised steel

then resistant to corrosion. Aluminium alloys are subject to stress corrosion.

The avoidance of potential crevices (*Figure 12.5*) which can hold water or some other electrolyte and so permit a cell to function, perhaps by bringing two dissimilar metals into electrical contact or by producing a concentration cell, should be avoided in design. Suitable design can also do much to reduce the incidence of stress corrosion.

Corrosion can be prevented or reduced by modification of the environment in which a metal is situated. Thus in the case of a packaged item an impervious packaging can be used so that water vapour cannot come into contact with the metal. Residual water vapour within the package can be removed by including a dessicant such as silica gel, within the package.

Where the environment adjacent to the metal is a liquid it is possible to add certain compounds to the liquid so that corrosion is inhibited, such additives being known as *inhibitors*. In the case of water-in-steel radiators or boilers, compounds which provide chromate or phosphate ions may be used as inhibitors, as they help to maintain the protective surface films on the steel.

One way of isolating a metal surface from the environment is to cover the metal with a protective coating, which can be impervious to oxygen, water or other pollutants. Coatings of grease, with perhaps the inclusion of specific corrosion inhibitors, can be used to give a temporary protective coating. Plasticised bitumens or resins can be used to give harder but still temporary coatings, while organic polymers or rubber latex can be applied to give coatings which can be stripped off when required.

One of the most common coatings applied to surfaces in order to prevent corrosion is paint, different types having different resistances to corrosion environments. Thus some paints have a good resistance to acids while others are good for water.

Steel components can be protected by dipping them in molten zinc to form a thin surface coating of zinc on the steel surface. This method is known as *galvanising*. The zinc acts as an anode with the steel being the cathode (*Figure 12.6*), and the zinc corrodes, rather than the steel, when the surface layer is broken. Small components can be coated with zinc by heating them in a closed container with zinc dust. This process is called *sheradising*.

Other metals can be used to coat steel, often by means of electroplating; thus nickel-plated steel offers some protection from the environment. Often a layer of chromium is applied to a steel surface over a base coat of nickel; the chromium layer is quite resistant to corrosion. Such coatings though offering protection are not so effective as zinc when the layer is broken, the zinc being sacrificed in place of the steel.

Steel surfaces are often treated with phosphoric acid or solutions containing phosphate ions, resulting in the formation of a phosphate coating, the process being known as *phosphating*. The coating bonds well with the surface and though giving some corrosion protection is generally used as a precursor for other coatings, perhaps paint.

Several metals can have corrosion-resistant surface layers produced by the application of solutions of chromates to their surfaces. A steel surface which has had the phosphating treatment may then be subject to a chromating treatment, the result being a good corrosion resistant surface layer on the metal.

Aluminium in the atmosphere has generally an oxide surface layer which offers some corrosion resistance and can be thickened by an electrolytic process. The treatment is known as *anodising*.

THE STABILITY OF POLYMERS

Polymers have maximum service temperatures of the order of 60° to 120°C, the value depending on the polymer concerned. While there is a quite significant deterioration of the tensile strength and hardness of thermoplastics below this temperature, thermosets are little affected. Thermoplastics, in particular, show creep and this is apparent at room temperature and increases quite markedly as the temperature is increased.

While some polymers are highly resistant to chemical attack, others are liable to stain, craze, soften, swell or dissolve completely. Thus, for instance, nylon shows little degradation with weak acids but is attacked by strong acids, it is resistant to alkalis and organic solvents. Polystyrene, however, though showing similar properties with acids and alkalis, is attacked by organic solvents. Polymers are generally resistant to water, hence their wide use for containers and pipes. However, there is generally a small amount of water absorption.

Polymers are generally affected by exposure to the atmosphere and sunlight. Ultra-violet light, present in sunlight, can cause a breakdown of the bonds in the polymer molecular chains and result in surface cracking. For this reason plastics often have a UV inhibitor mixed with the polymer when the material is compounded. Deterioration in colour and transparency can also occur. Most thermoplastics are affected by ultra-violet light, particularly cellulose derivatives and, to a limited extent, nylon and polyethylene.

Natural rubber is resistant to most acids and alkalis, however its resistance to petroleum products is poor. It also deteriorates rapidly in sunlight. Some synthetic rubbers such as neoprene, are more resistant to petroleum products and sunlight. Ozone can cause cracking of natural rubber, and many synthetic rubbers. Neoprene is one of the rubbers having a high resistance to ozone.

THE STABILITY OF CERAMICS

Ceramics are relatively stable when exposed to the atmosphere, though the presence of sulphur dioxide in the atmosphere and its subsequent change to sulphuric acid can result in deterioration of ceramics. Thus building materials such as stone and brick can be severly damaged by exposure to industrial atmosphere in which sulphur dioxide is present.

Damage to ceramics may also result from the freezing of water which has become absorbed into pores of the material and from thermal shock. The low thermal conductivity of ceramics can result in large thermal gradients being set up and hence considerable stresses. This can lead to flaking of the surface. Ceramics used as furnace linings may well be affected by molten metals or slags. Furnace linings need to be chosen with care.

PROBLEMS

1 It has been observed that cars in a dry desert part of a country remain remarkably free of rust when compared with cars in a damp climate such as England. Offer an explanation for this.

2 Why does the de-aeration of water in a boiler reduce corrosion?

3 What criteria should be used if corrosion is to be kept to a low value when two dissimilar metals are joined together?

4 Aluminium pipes are to be used to carry water into a water tank. Possible materials for the tank are copper or galvanised steel. Which material would you advocate if corrosion is to be minimised?

5 It is found that for a junction between mild steel and copper in a sea water environment that the mild steel corrodes rather than the copper. With a mild steel – aluminium junction in the same environment it is found that the aluminium corrodes more than the mild steel. Explain the above observations.

6 Pieces of magnesium placed close to buried iron pipes are used to reduce the corrosion of the iron. Explain.

7 Corrosion of a stainless steel flange is found to occur when a lead gasket is used. Explain.

8 Propose a method to give galvanic protection for a steel water storage tank.

9 Why should copper piping not be used to supply water to a galvanised steel water storage tank?

10 What are the main ways galvanic cells can be set up in metals?

11 Compare the use of zinc and tin as protective coatings for steel.

12 The following note appeared in the Products and Techniques section of *Engineering*. Explain the purpose and mode of action of the anodes referred to in the note.
"Corrosion anodes
Solid anodes for the cathodic protection of water tanks are now available in a variety of sizes and three types – freestanding, suspended and weld attached. No prior preparation is required before installation, and protection begins at once. Being non-toxic, the Metalife anodes can be used in tanks for drinking water. Belonza Molecular Metalife Ltd, Harrogate."

13 What further information do you think you would need to assess the merits of the anodes referred to in the previous question? Do you think it would matter what type of material the water tank was made of?

14 In an article on underwater equipment design the author states that good design required the avoidance of crevices and high stress concentrations and that also the number of different metals should be kept to a minimum. Give explanations for these criteria.

13 Choosing materials

This chapter brings together the various aspects covered in earlier chapters and gives you practice in making a choice of materials for components.

THE REQUIREMENTS   What functions does a component have to perform? What are the essential requirements of the component in order that it can fulfil those functions? These are two important questions that require answers before either the materials or the forming or fabrication processes can be established.

For instance, the functions of a domestic kitchen pan may be deemed to be: to hold liquid and allow it to be heated to temperatures of the order of 100°C. In order to do this, the container must not deform when heated to these temperatures. It must be a good conductor of heat. It must be leak proof. It must not ignite when in contact with a flame or hot electrical element. No doubt you can think of other essential requirements. There can also be other requirements which, though not essential, are desirable. For instance, the surface finish of the pan must look attractive.

From such an analysis of functions and requirements can come a list of the essential and desirable characteristics required of the material to be used for the object. The following are some of the common characteristics that could be required:

1 Certain mechanical properties such as strength, hardness, stiffness, fatigue resistance.

2 Certain behaviour in specific environments, e.g. corrosion free in a marine environment.

3 Electrical or thermal properties, e.g. an electrical insulator or perhaps a good conductor of heat.

4 Ability to be formed or fabricated to meet the requirements of the objects's shape, dimensions, etc.

5 A cost factor.

The choice of forming or fabrication process, or processes, will depend on a number of factors. The following are some possible factors:

1 The quantity of items required and the required production rate.

2 The dimensional accuracy required.

3 The surface finish required.

4 The size of the items, i.e. both overall size and section thickness.

5 The requirement for holes, inserts and undercuts.

6 The type of material being used.

7 A cost factor.

In the case of the domestic kitchen pan, the requirement that the material be a good conductor of heat reduces the consideration to metals, particularly when taken together with the requirement that the material can be put in contact with a flame and contain hot liquids up to 100°C. A deep drawing process might be considered suitable with aluminium as the specified material. Being a cold working process this will give a good surface finish. But what about the pan handle? What material should be used for it? How should it be fastened to the pan? Perhaps it should not be fastened but produced in the same process as the pan.

PROBLEMS

1 *A towel rail*

A simple towel rail consisting of a tube or rod held by clamps at each end to the wall is proposed. The towel rail is for use in the steamy atmosphere of the bathroom. The towel rails are to be mass produced and have to be cheap. The rail needs to withstand not only the weight of wet towels but also a person partially supporting their weight against the rail without any permanent bend being produced or indeed any significant bending under such loads.

(a) What are the crucial factors that determine the type of material that can be used?

(b) Suggest some possible materials.

(c) What determines whether a tube or rod is used? What determines the thickness of the tube or the diameter of the rod?

(d) What factors affect the cost of the finished component?

(e) Propose a possible specification for the material.

2 *A simple spanner*

A mass production method is required for the production of spanners for sale as cheap items for the do-it-yourself enthusiast. The material used should be relatively cheap but able to withstand the uses to which the spanner will be put.

(a) What factors determine the type of material that can be used?

(b) What processing methods are feasible, bearing in mind the need to produce a cheap product?

(c) Specify a possible material and appropriate processing.

3 *An electric plug case*

Examine a 13 A mains electric plug. Such plugs are mass produced and cheap. They have to be designed so that they are cheap to produce and able to cope with the various terminals, fuse and connecting screws that are needed. They have to be electrically safe.

(a) What functions are required of the plug material?

(b) What materials would you suggest for the plug case? On what basis did you decide on the materials?

(c) What processes would you suggest for the production of the plug case? How are the processes determined by the material used? How are the material and process determined by the cost?

4 *Motor car body*

For this problem you may like to consult 'The Open University, A second level course, An introduction to Materials Units 12 and 13, Car body'. Present day car bodies generally are made from mild steel with a carbon content of less than 0.1 per cent. The steel, in the form of thin sheet, is pressed into the required shapes.

(a) What functions are required of the car body which dictate the type of material used and the processes employed to shape the material? Consider the requirements to apply to mass produced cars selling at the lower end of the car market.

(b) Why is mild steel preferred over other materials?

(c) What would be the problems in the use of plastics for a car body?

(d) What are the problems associated with the use of mild steel for car bodies?

5 *A street lamp support pole*

Consider the design and the materials employed for the street lamp support poles. Typical materials used are reinforced concrete, carbon steel and cast iron.

(a) What functions are required of the material used as a street lamp support pole?

(b) What processes might be used for the production of street lamp support poles?

(c) What part do you think cost plays in determining the material and process used?

(d) What part do you think ease of maintenance plays in determining the material used?

(e) Consider the production of a street lamp pole as an aluminium or steel extrusion. How would such materials behave in service? What would happen to the two materials if a car collided with the pole, i.e. a sudden impact?

6 *A Coca-Cola container*

(a) Coca-Cola can be purchased in glass or plastic bottles and aluminium cans. What are the properties required of the material used for the container?

(b) What are the factors which lead to glass, plastic and aluminium being used for the container?

(c) What are the advantages and disadvantages of the materials currently used for the container?

7 *A screwdriver*

The typical screwdriver is a steel driver in a plastic handle. Such items are mass produced and relatively cheap. They have to be able to withstand torques being applied to the driver without the driver becoming damaged or broken and also without rotating independently of the handle.

(a) What functions are required of (i) the driver material, (ii) the handle material?

(b) What types of material would be suitable for (i) the driver, (ii) the handle?

(c) What processes could be used to produce (i) the driver, (ii) the handle?

(d) How could the driver be joined suitably with the handle? What are the problems to be overcome in the joining process?

8 *A car exhaust system*

Car exhaust systems appear in practice to have a relatively short life before corrosion damage becomes so serious that a replacement exhaust system is required.

(a) What conditions are exhaust systems subject to in use?

(b) What properties are required of the materials used for exhaust systems?

(c) What materials might be suitable for exhaust systems?

(d) What materials are generally used?

9 *Flexible foam plastics as packing material*

Polyether foam is used widely as a packing material where goods need to be protected against shock and vibration. The material can be cut to the shape of the object being packaged and so enable the object to be completely surrounded by foam. Frequently however the object being packaged is not completely surrounded but held between pads or corner blocks of the foam.

(a) How is the foam able to protect the packaged object against shock?

(b) What properties are required of the foam? How rigid do you think the foam should be?

(c) What type of tests might be carried out to test the efficiency of a particular foam packaging material and the way it is used?

10 *Small boats*

(a) What properties are required of the material used for the hull of a small boat?

(b) Materials that have been used for small boats' hulls are wood, metals and composites such as glass-reinforced polyester resin. How do the properties of these materials compare with those required?

(c) What are the processes used to produce boat hulls from these materials?

(d) What factors do you consider determine the choice of material for a small boat hull?

Index